DARWIN:
BEFORE AND AFTER

DARWIN:
BEFORE AND AFTER

An Evangelical Assessment

By

ROBERT E. D. CLARK, M.A., Ph.D.

06796

MOODY PRESS
CHICAGO

CONTENTS

" An enthusiast sways humanity by . . . dinning it into our ears that this or that question has only one possible solution; but when once he is gone an army of quiet and uninfluential people set to work and remind us of the other side and demolish the generous imposture."

R. L. STEVENSON

CHAPTER I

GERMS OF LIFE

WE LIVE ON THE SURFACE OF A TINY PLANET, POISED in empty space. No matter in what direction we turn our vision, there is little to be seen save white-hot and red-hot stars. Apparently we live alone in a universe as inhospitable as we could well imagine it to be. Even if other beings do happen to exist in the vast expanse of space, we are isolated from them by distances so immense that it would take light tens if not hundreds of thousands of years to traverse the distances that separate them from ourselves. Our isolation could hardly be more complete. Yet here on earth we live, tender fragile creatures that seem to be altogether out of place in such a cosmos.

How did we get here? That is an all absorbing question about which mankind has speculated for thousands of years. And still he speculates and will continue to do so until the close of history.

It is with the story of these speculations that this book is concerned; the fascinating story of man's search for truth about the past, his advance in knowledge and understanding, followed by his all too frequent perversion of that knowledge, which turned science into the tool of prejudice and the creator of misery. All these things and more are enshrined in the story of evolution.

*   *   *   *   *

How did man arise?

In ancient times, Anaximander drew attention to the obvious fact that if the first generation of men had started off their careers in the form that all men started them in his day, namely as babies, they would undoubtedly have perished as a result of exposure to the elements. So he made another suggestion.   Being very interested in sharks, he imagined, naturally enough, that he could see a remarkable likeness between these aquatic animals and *homo sapiens*.   He suggested, accordingly, that the first men had been derived from a species of fish.   He seems to have thought that these fish were possessed of kangaroo-like pockets into which their young could retreat in time of danger.   Finally, these remarkable creatures reached the sea-shore and, preferring the dry land to their natural habitat, they changed their ways and turned into men.   It was as simple as that.

Later, Empedocles propounded a different scheme. Strange changes took place in prehistoric plants as a result of which they produced parts of animals instead of leaves and flowers.   All kinds of gruesome parts were formed— heads, arms, shoulders, and eyes without sockets.   Then love triumphed over hate and the parts sought each other out.   But since they became joined to one another by chance, they produced bizarre monsters only.   Some of these were animals with heads of men and men with heads of animals.   Quasi-human creatures were there, in the disordered medley, with double chests and two heads. These extraordinary monsters soon died out, for they could neither live for long nor propagate their kind. Gradually, once again by chance, forms capable of reproduction arose.   Among these the fittest survived and the rest passed into oblivion.

In ancient times evolutionary views of this kind were only vaguely expressed in words—so vaguely that it is often only too easy for us to read our own beliefs into the writings of these ancient scholars.   We must remember that, no matter how attractive or how " modern " their views may seem to us, the real motive in those days was to explain the origin of everything in terms of the interacting forces of nature—symbolized by love and hate.   Not till the time of Aristotle—the imperially-sponsored scientist for whom

2,000 naturalists regularly collected specimens—do we find the real beginnings of biology.

As the years passed by the amazingly free speculations of the early Greeks came to be examined in detail and the wilder speculations were dismissed, one by one. By Aristotle's time the possibility that one species might gradually change into another had been finally rejected— no doubt for the very good reason that no one had ever seen it happen. Nor was the need for such a view any longer apparent. Observation had shown, on unnumbered occasions, that creatures could be spontaneously generated from mud and slime. On this point experience and even experiment were so convincing that, so far at least as insects were concerned, no one had ever even thought of doubting it. It was generally supposed, too, that higher animals might be generated in the same way and Aristotle was disposed to wonder whether the same might not apply to men. For how else could one account for the strange races of men that travellers had reported from far-away lands—men small and men large; black, yellow and white? Who could tell? Perchance a race of warriors might emerge one night from a slimy pool not far from where you chanced to live, and lay siege to your city in the morning. But on this matter the great scholar was cautious, for no one had ever *seen* men being generated out of slime, though they had certainly seen flies, fishes and worms being produced in this remarkable way.

Such views were in accord with the philosophy of the time. Plato had elaborated the theory that form was immutable and his view came to be widely accepted among the Greeks. It was contrary to sound reason, therefore, to suppose that the essential structures of living things could change. But since the form or, as we might put it to-day, the " blue-print " of an animal continued to exist in the non-material world whether the animal in question lived on earth or not, spontaneous generation was easy to imagine. For, after all, the structure of the generated animal did not really arise *de novo* but was already in existence in the spiritual world first of all.

Not only was spontaneous generation from slime a perfectly possible and natural occurrence, but the ancients were also convinced that living creatures did not always reproduce +heir kind. In ancient times, for instance, the drone fly was believed to be a honey-bee and to be generated from the carcasses of cattle. When the local supply of honey was low, an ox would be killed and the drone-flies that hatched from its carcase would be set free to replenish the bee-population of the countryside.[1] The ease with which such beliefs came to be accepted made the origin of life far less of a problem in early times than it is to-day.

In the history of thought, perhaps, there is no fact more striking than the way in which an apparent solution to a problem has closed the prospects of further advance. To the ancients, the various suggestions that had been made to explain the origin of things must have seemed like brilliant discoveries. The coming of mankind into the world could easily be ascribed to fish-like ancestors, to sex, or to spontaneous generation from slime—but with each of these solutions men remained satisfied, convinced that a merely verbal answer was all that was required of them. This tendency to become hypnotized by words has always been one of humanity's greatest failings and there are many people even to-day who never pause to think whether an alleged explanation increases their understanding of nature or whether its appeal lies wholly in long, well-sounding, pseudo-scientific words.

In later times Christians, like pagans, were often apt to fall into the same error, imagining that every mystery could be solved by ascribing things to God. Yet, rightly understood, a belief in God as Creator is a real step forward

[1] See C. R. Osten-Sacken, *On the Oxen-born Bees of the Ancients*, Heidelberg, 1894.

in the understanding and unification of nature, for it is
the belief that somehow or other the way in which things
were made bears a resemblance to the way in which man
makes things—by formulating and executing a plan. The
possibility that this view may not be factually correct is
beside the point ; to the simple mind, God may prove as
real an explanation as the explanations of physical science.
A belief in God as Creator may bring about an enlargement
of understanding, whereas the mere assertion that " spontaneous generation " did the trick tells us nothing at all
because it appeals to no answering chord within.

It was thus that Christianity led the way, falteringly at
first, but later much more definitely, to a rational view of
nature. In the early ages Christians saw clearly enough
that if pagans insisted on making slime the cause of all
things there was no room for a Creator-God. St. Gregory
did great service by urging on these grounds that spontaneous generation must be false. It appears that this was
the first serious criticism that the doctrine ever received
and it is important to notice that until this doctrine was
overthrown, biology as a science was well-nigh impossible.
Moreover, by recognizing God as the source of created
things, Christianity made possible the reverent attention
to detail that is necessary before science can begin. If
things happen anyhow, if they happen spontaneously,
there is little incentive to discover *how* they happen, little
incentive to look into the countless details and intricacies
that are present in every living creature. That Christians
in the early ages were often prejudiced and unscientific in
their attitude (of what body of men may this not be said ?)
there is no reason to deny, but despite all that may be said
on this score, it was Christianity that first pointed the way
to a right and healthy attitude towards nature.

Throughout the Middle Ages, the doctrine of spontaneous generation was still widely accepted. But it often
flourished in a form that almost belied its name. Many of

those who held it were convinced that it was only apparent. God, they believed, had created seeds of every living thing —seeds that floated in the wind, too small to be seen or separated from the air—and these began to grow wherever conditions were favourable. In this way spontaneous generation—which in those days seemed to be an observable fact—was made consistent with a belief in God as Creator. However, this doctrine of seeds was not invoked for man and the higher animals but only for insects, fishes and plants. Among these there seemed to be definite evidence for spontaneous generation. Indeed, only by a careful scientific technique could it be proved definitely that the latter was *not* taking place—and this was by no means an easy matter.

The doctrine of spontaneous generation was slow in dying. William Harvey, in his famous work *De Generatione Animalium* (1651), is generally credited with being the first to have overthrown it since he taught that all living things arise from " eggs " (*omne vivum ex ovo*). But in fact Harvey was by no means so clear in his own mind as his oft-quoted words might lead us to suppose. He certainly thought that it was a rule of nature that life arose from eggs, yet it would seem that at times he wavered and began to wonder whether there were exceptions to the rule.[1]   However this may be, he boldly sponsored the view that eggs or seeds of life may yet exist, even in cases where they are so small as to be quite invisible and un- detectable.   " Many animals, especially insects," he writes, " arise and are propagated from elements and seeds so small as to be invisible (like atoms flying in the air), scattered and dispersed here and there by the winds ; and yet these

[1] See A. W. Meyer, *An Analysis of the De Generatione Animalium of William Harvey*, 1936. Meyer concludes : " It seems . . . to me that Harvey seriously doubted that the living can arise from the non-living and that he had hoped to demonstrate the untenability of such an assumption, but found himself baffled in all directions " (p. 53). See also H. Driesch (*The History and Theory of Vitalism*. 1914, p. 26), who maintains that Harvey is merely contradicting Aristotle's view that germs are different from eggs.

animals are supposed to have arisen spontaneously, or from decomposition, because their ova are nowhere to be found."[1]

Here, in these words, we have an example of the kind of reasoning that has so often opened the way to new horizons of knowledge. It is the faith that interprets the seen in terms of the unseen, the visible in terms of the invisible. The history of science is the denial of the philosophy of positivism, the doctrine that statements are " meaningless " if they attribute visible effects to something that is *invisible* and that lies behind nature.

" We say," says Ayer, " that a sentence is factually significant to any given person, if, and only if, he knows how to verify the proposition which it purports to express."[2] Had such a view been heeded in the past it is doubtful whether much advance could ever have been made in any branch of natural science. The existence of germs, atoms, and the unconscious mind, to say nothing of many other great achievements of science, would never have been discovered.

Later in the 17th century Redi studied the commonest of all supposed instances of spontaneous generation—the formation of worms in meat. In those days little fodder was available for cattle in the winter time and they were mostly killed before the cold months set in. The larders of the rich were well stocked with meat which, after months of storage, began to lose its freshness—there were no domestic refrigerators in those days.

It is no wonder, then, that instances of worms appearing on the meat stored in larders were widespread. These alone were enough to convince most naturalists of the truth of spontaneous generation. Redi disproved this explanation by covering the meat so that flies could not lay eggs upon it and after this worms were no longer produced. He concluded that spontaneous generation was a mistake—although he was still unable to explain in detail how it was that insects sometimes entered plants

[1] Willis edition of Harvey's *Works*, 1847, p. 321.
[2] A. J. Ayer, *Language, Truth and Logic*, 1936, p. 19.

or how parasites (e.g. tapeworms) entered the bodies of animals. Nevertheless, other naturalists soon followed him in rejecting the doctrine of spontaneous generation and, for a while, it seemed likely that the latter would be finally discredited. In the end, however, this was not so. Experiments, performed in the seventeenth century, which should have been conclusive, had to be repeated in the nineteenth. Not until the well-known work of Pasteur was the myth of spontaneous generation finally exploded, at least, in the minds of most men of science—though even to-day, as we shall later see, there are those who still cannot rid their minds entirely of the ancient superstition.

Why did it prove so difficult to overthrow the notion of spontaneous generation ? Why did those who were determined to believe the doctrine at all costs refuse to accept the outcome of Redi's experiments—preferring always to think that, if only the right conditions could be found, living things would arise from non-living ?

It is to philosophic and religious opinions, rather than to science, that we must look in order to answer this question.

Healthy Christian thought had always been sceptical about spontaneous generation. St. Augustine had argued that it was absurd to suppose that God would have told Noah to build an ark to preserve the animals, if they would in any case have been generated anew from the slime and mud remaining after the deluge. Gregory, as we have seen, had denied the doctrine on theological grounds. Christians who accepted the doctrine often did so superficially only in deference to the supposed facts, and with profound misgivings. But there was another philosophy abroad—the mystic and rationalistic doctrine of those who sought to identify God with His Creation. We see it in Ralph Cudworth, the Cambridge Platonist, with his theory of " Plastic Nature "—" neither God nor Goddess, but a Low and Imperfect Creature " which severally organizes and frames all things that " transcend the Power of Fortuitous

Mechanism"; [1] we see it in the Jesuit J. T. Needham with his corporeal non-intelligent force that turns a tiny germ into a body; in Spinoza the "God-intoxicated atheist" who made out that the forces of nature could very well do everything for which God had hitherto been invoked and were, in fact, identical with God. And in many other writings of the period, the old Aristotelian idea that there are secret forces of nature which are unconscious but semi-intelligent, found expression again and again. For such a view was inherited from the ancients through centuries of tradition and was not to be thrown aside as a result of a few experiments by naturalists.

According to the ancient pagan thinkers the world enacted an endless cycle of events—it had neither beginning nor end. The coming and going of life was merely one feature of the cosmic drama, as spontaneous and as natural as the rolling of the spheres. Life arose from the dust and turned to dust again, the one as spontaneously as the other. No wonder, then, if the denial that slime and sunlight can produce life has always seemed like invoking creation by a Deity who is beyond and outside of nature, the very thing the rationalists and theological immanentists of all ages have been out to avoid.

This tradition of thought has continued right on to present times. Haeckel claimed that spontaneous generation must be true, not because its truth could be confirmed in the laboratory, but because, otherwise, it would be necessary to believe in a Creator. [2] Pouchet, the bitter enemy of Pasteur, held similar views. He mockingly argued that if the air really contained seeds of life as Pasteur supposed, the seeds would have to be so numerous that the air would be choked with them. How else, he asked, could the seed of a rare fungus be deposited faithfully on a speck only 0.00155 square inches in area? If Pasteur was right, the

---

[1] R. Cudworth, *System of the Universe*, 1678, p. 190, etc.

[2] Compare the remark of Sir Charles Lyell : " The German critics have attacked me vigorously, saying that by the impugning of the doctrine of spontaneous generation, I have left them nothing but the direct and miraculous intervention of the First Cause." (*Life*, I, 467.)

seeds would have to be so numerous that " the air in which we live ought to have almost the density of iron." It was so much easier to believe that spontaneous generation was *really* spontaneous than to explain it away by means of invisible and undetectable germs of matter floating about in the air. The old philosophers, he said, had peopled the air with sylphs, the new ones with germs.

In England we have the same story. H. C. Bastian (1837–1915), an ardent rationalist, devoted the energies of a lifetime to a misguided attempt to overthrow the work of Pasteur. Bastian was a pioneer in the study of aphasia but he tended to despise his own valuable neurological work which had brought him fame and for which he has been elected to the Royal Society. He was deeply hurt when the Royal Society refused to publish his papers on spontaneous generation.[1]

Spontaneous generation, in short, has always appealed to those whose passionate desire is to avoid belief in the transcendental God of Christianity. If only it can be urged that the apparently blind forces of nature are in reality intelligent —or apparently intelligent—so that life can arise from the non-living by the operation of ordinary laws of nature; then only is there a chance of avoiding the view that God has intervened in the course of things, and created living things. The harm and suffering that this perverted desire has done to mankind in the course of history is incalculable. Even in ancient times the germ theory of disease was widely known and accepted among simple people. But the scholars of classical times would have none of it—preferring to believe in the spontaneous generation of the microbe enemies of mankind. Had it not been for rationalism and mystic theology the views of Redi and William Harvey would doubtless have been finally established in the seventeenth century and have led on to aseptic surgery without delay. As it was, mankind had to wait until the nineteenth century before all the clever subterfuges of the spontaneous generationists

[1] See *Proc. Roy. Soc.*, 1917, **89B**, xxi. Also Bastian's books on spontaneous generation.

had been finally overthrown; then it was that Pasteur's convincing experiments at once suggested to Lister the need for preventing infection during surgical operations.

But we must continue our story. The fundamental problem was the age-long question: "How do living things arise?" Rationalists of all ages had attempted to solve the mystery by the theory of spontaneous generation. In time that view became impossible. Under the influence of the Christian Church the old notion that even men could be spontaneously generated had long been given up —though the possibility was still held in the case of lower organisms. Harvey's dictum had taken its place. But once again this only threw the difficulty a stage further back. It was easy to say that life came from eggs—but how did eggs arise? How did living things emerge from eggs? These were questions that could not be avoided.

Once again, thinkers separated into two warring camps. Unable to abandon the idea that, somehow or other, spontaneous generation was the solution to every mystery, many biologists began, in effect, to assert that living things were spontaneously generated, not this time from slime, but from eggs! They pictured the eggs as containing amorphous matter that slowly shaped itself into animals: a doctrine that came to be called *epigenesis*. Others (the so-called *pre-formationists*), on the other hand, maintained that the egg itself contained a " germ " that was the essence of the living animal. They held that the tiny animal or man "unfolded" in the egg—becoming larger and perhaps chang-ing its form, like the Japanese flowers of our childhood days when they were placed in water. This unfolding was called *evolution*, and its very existence was denied by the epigenesists. Although, to-day, the word *evolution* is applied to the story of the development of the race rather than to that of the individual, the two subjects are so closely interconnected, as we shall shortly see, that it is impossible to tell the story of the one without reference to the story of the other.

CHAPTER II

MEN WITHIN MEN

NO CONJUROR HAS EVER DONE WHAT NATURE DOES so easily. The miracle of a new animal, or a new human being, born from an egg, is still to-day, as it was in ancient times, the most surprising thing we know of in the entire universe. It seems altogether incredible that our complicated bodies should slowly and solemnly emerge from mere eggs—yet that is the fact to be explained.

Man's earliest attempts to understand the mystery did not go very far. He could do little more than suggest analogies between growth in the womb and other less mysterious processes of nature—one of which was the making of cheese. Job, for instance, enquired of his Maker : " Hast thou not poured me out as milk, and curdled me like cheese ? " (Job 10 : 10).

In the fifth century B.C. Empedocles sought to probe more deeply into the matter. He concluded that : " Sinews are formed from a mixture of equal parts of earth and air, nails are water congealed . . . bones are formed from a mixture of equal parts of water and earth." Sweat and tears, he said, were made of four parts of fire and one of water. About the same time Hippocrates tried to explain the resemblance between children and their parents. He maintained that particles come together from every part of the parent's body and go to form the offspring. This ancient view was, as we shall see, revived again in modern times.

Aristotle (fourth century B.C.) was the first to make a clear distinction between the two views which, in later times, came to be known as *preformationism* and *epigenesis*. According to the first view the embryo is present all the time, though too small to be seen, until, in the process of growth, it unfolds itself and becomes visible. According to the second, it is supposed that new structures actually come into existence during growth.

Aristotle set himself the task of finding out which of these two views was correct. He argued to himself that if a chicken in a hen's egg merely increases in size, the larger organs ought to become visible before the smaller ones. Thus the lung, being larger, should appear before the heart. He found, however, that this was the converse of what actually happened, for the heart became visible first.

For Aristotle there was nothing illogical or unnatural in such a conclusion. Since he believed that amorphous slime could generate worms, insects, rats and mice, what was there to prevent the amorphous contents of an egg from generating new structures during the development of a chick ? But in later times, when spontaneous generation was in the process of being overthrown, the position was different. Epigenesis was a form of spontaneous generation and tended to be accepted by those who, like J. T. Needham, were keen supporters of that theory.

In this, as in other matters, the views of later times were mainly dominated by Aristotle, and, with the exception of a few ancient writers, such as Seneca, it was not until 1625 that Joseph of Aromatari again suggested preformationism. In seeds and bulbs he had noticed the complete plant folded up, and he generalized from this to hens and human beings. But most naturalists, including William Harvey, continued to hold the epigenetic view, and it was not until 1672 that preformationism came into its own, and was destined to dominate biological thought for a century.

In August of that year Malpighi was experimenting with hens' eggs in the heat of the Italian summer. He left his eggs overnight and the excessive heat began to incubate them so that when he opened them next day he found structures that corresponded with those of hatched chickens. " When we inquire carefully into the production of animals out of their eggs," he writes, " we always find the animal there, so that our labour is repaid and we see an emerging manifestation of parts successively, but never the first origin of any of them." These remarks applied, of course, to fertilized eggs. Malpighi never claimed to have seen a chicken in an egg before it had been fertilized.

Leeuwenhoek's famous discovery of animalcules (now called *spermatozoa*) in the seminal fluid took place about this time (1677). Examining the liquid with a microscope, this famous naturalist was astonished to see a multitude of tadpole-like creatures swimming about. At first he thought they were caused by disease, but soon he convinced himself that they could be seen in the seminal fluid of all male animals. Here, then, he had discovered something that was obviously profoundly connected with the mysterious subject of generation : something that naturalists had failed to observe before[1] ; something that would inevitably overturn all previous theories on the subject.

Leeuwenhoek was wild with enthusiasm. Like many another before and since his time, he allowed his enthusiasm to get the better of his powers of observation. In time, he was able—or rather thought he was able—to distinguish male and female spermatozoa in the seminal fluid. At times, it seems, he even supposed that the tiny creatures were endowed with the instincts of adults for, in a letter to Boerhaave, he tells us that in the seminal fluid of the ram he observed the little animalcules marching in flocks like sheep !

Before long, others began to improve upon these startling stories. Hartsoeker, Dalenpatius and Gautier all asserted that they had seen exceedingly minute forms of

---

[1] A search in the Classics soon revealed several suggestions (by Plato, Aristotle, Hippocrates and Democritus) to the effect that men were derived from worms—which suggested that, just possibly, this knowledge had been known to some of the ancients. Nor is this at all unlikely, for lenses were known in Roman times. Plano-convex lenses have been found at Gnossus ; Nero, being shortsighted, is said to have watched his gladiators through a glass. (See A. W. Meyer, *Rise of Embryology*, chap. XII).

men, with heads and legs complete, inside spermatozoa. Gautier went so far as to say that he had seen a tiny horse (he published a picture of it) in the semen of a horse, an animalcule with very large ears in the semen of a donkey and, finally, minute cocks in the semen of a cock. In 1699 there was published the notorious letter of Plantade (" M. Dalenpatius ") on these miniature beings. " They move," he says, " with extraordinary agility and by the lashing of their tails they produce and agitate the wavelets in which they swim. Who would have believed that in them was a human body ? But I have seen this thing with my own eyes. For a while I was examining them all with care, one appeared which was larger than the others, and sloughed off the skin in which it had been enclosed, and clearly revealed, free from covering, both its skin, its legs, its breast and two arms, while the cast skin, when pulled further up, enveloped the head after the manner of a cowl. It was impossible to distinguish sexual characters on account of its small size, and it died in the act of uncovering itself . . . diagrams are attached."

Even this was not the end of these wild fancies. It was claimed by some that animalcules married and had children, that young and old could be distinguished and that some had two heads, like human monsters. Yet others claimed that the animalcules floated about in the air, ready to enter the bodies of potential parents unawares ![1] In a delightful satire of these reports, published in 1750, " Sir " John Hill claimed that, by means of " a wonderful cylindrical, caloptrical, rotundoconcavo-convex Machine " of his own invention, he had been able to catch small specks of " dust " carried on the west wind, which turned out to be little men and women.

[1] A view that lingered on into the present century. See F. Hovenden, *What is Life ?* (1897 and 1909), who supposed that the discovery of the rare gases in the atmosphere was really the discovery of the animalcules ! " Sir " John Hill's satire, *Lucina sine Concubitu*, which was published pseudonymously, has been reprinted in recent times (Edinburgh, 1885).

Many and wild were the speculations that these discoveries, both real and imaginary, produced in their day. Hitherto it had been the received opinion that the whole of the seminal fluid was concerned in generation. Leeuwenhoek now put forward the novel—and, as we now know, correct—idea, that only *one* of the spermatozoons is involved. But from this he argued, quite wrongly, that only the male was concerned in the production of offspring, the female being a mere receptacle for the seed. Others, such as Buffon, believed that the newly discovered objects were the parts or "atoms," derived from the various organs of the body, which enabled the offspring to inherit the qualities of its parents.

The immediate effect of the new discovery was to establish preformationism. For the first time in history it seemed that a final refutation of Aristotle's *epigenesis* was at hand. The spermatozoa were actually visible ; the very same spermatozoa that were destined to "evolve" into adult animals and human beings. Certainly they bore no close resemblance to the animals they were going to produce ; few reputable authorities believed the stories of tiny animals seen in seminal fluids. But then tadpoles did not resemble frogs, nor caterpillars butterflies, yet no one had ever suggested that the latter were generated spontaneously from the former. It was obvious enough, to all who thought philosophically, that the various organs of tadpoles and caterpillars did not finish up just anywhere in the frogs and butterflies, but that the latter were, at least in some sense, "preformed" in the former. In the same way the various parts of the spermatozoon must be destined to produce the various parts of the adult animal. It was beside the point if, as Aristotle had found, a small organ like the heart developed before a large organ like the lung, for it was still clear that structures were previously present capable of producing both heart and lung. Preformationists had no reason to believe that each of the many metamorphoses involved in the growth of an animal must start at the *same* time and proceed at the *same* rate.

Such was the essential viewpoint of the preformationists. From the very first Malpighi had never claimed that, at an early stage, a chick had precisely the same shape as the fowl into which it was later to be transformed; rather he saw that there was an unequal unfolding of the parts and as time passed by he emphasized the inequality of this unfolding more and more. Some preformationists, however, went to extremes and brought the whole doctrine into disrepute—a disrepute from which it is only now beginning to recover.

Later the preformationists divided into two parties. Some (*animalculists*) held that living organisms were somehow folded up inside the males, while others (*ovists*) said they were present in the females. And just as the eye of faith had been well able to discern all the forms it wished to see in the spermatozoa, so an equally abundant amount of evidence was soon furnished by those who were able to see full-grown animals in unfertilized eggs.

The true view—the view that the spermatozoon pierces the ovum, causing the latter to divide and develop, so that progeny are derived not from one but from *both* their parents—was first suggested by George Garden in 1693. In those days the spermatozoa were being compared freely to worms and snakes and the statement in the Bible which says that the seed of the woman (the ovum !) shall bruise the head of the serpent (spermatozoon !) (Gen. 3 : 15), a passage which Garden misapplied with enthusiasm, apparently suggested the idea to his mind.[1]

* * * *

Preformation soon found its place in theology and philosophy. Swammerdam, as a result of a suggestion made by Malebranche, used it to explain original sin. He said that if we were present inside our parents when they

[1] *Philosophical Transactions*, 1693, **17**, 414.

sinned, it followed that we, being a part of them, must have sinned too.

The difficulty of this position was that it obviated the necessity for baptism, for if we were curled up inside our parents when they were baptized it followed that there could be no need for us to be baptized again. The theologians of the day discussed this question with their customary gravity, but could reach no conclusion. The difficulty certainly did not curb the wild activity of Swammerdam's brain. He even went so far as to produce a delightful proof of pre-formation from the Bible. According to *Hebrews* 7: 9-10, Levi paid tithes before he was born and must, therefore, have existed as a tiny little fellow inside Abraham when the latter gave tithes to Melchisedek, King of Salem !

Preformationism was further developed by the well-known French philosopher Malebranche. Swammerdam had argued that if people were inside one another like box within box, the human race would suddenly come to an end when the last box was reached. Malebranche dis-agreed with this conclusion. He could see no reason why the encasements should not extend infinitely. Every tree, he maintained, contained another tree inside every one of its germ cells, these in turn contained smaller trees with still smaller trees inside these, and so *ad infinitum*. And why not ? Such a view could only appear ridiculous to those who limited the power of Almighty God by their own senses and limited imagination. " We see in the germ of a fresh egg which has not been incubated an entirely formed chicken," he wrote. " We see frogs in frogs' eggs and we shall see other animals in their germs also when we have sufficient skill and experience to dis-cover them. We must suppose that all the bodies of men and animals which will be born until the consummation of time will have been direct products of the original crea-tion ; in other words, that the first females were created with all the subsequent individuals of their own species within them. We might push this thought further and belike with much reason and truth, but we not unreasonably fear a too premature penetration into the works of God."

Before his death in 1725 Hartsoeker, who had published one of the best pictures of a baby sitting in a spermatozoon, and who had done so much to found the preformationist doctrine, abandoned it as a result of a calculation which he made on the size of rabbits. He estimated that, on the preformationist theory, the rabbits that were running across the meadows so happily in the early eighteenth century must have been less than a ten thousand millionth of their present size when they were created inside their first parent in the year 4004 B.C. He found it quite impossible to imagine such small rabbits, so he abandoned his views on preformation.

Even this calculation was not enough to convince all his contemporaries. In 1729 Bourguet revised the mathematics and showed that it was not necessary to assume that the smallest rabbits at the time of the creation were less than about a six hundred and thirty-one millionth of their present size, which, he said, was by no means an impossible figure.

In time the inevitable happened. These fantastic speculations and calculations served to bring preformationism into disrepute. The sound common sense and appreciation of scientific principles upon which this doctrine had been based were forgotten and in time the very word " preformation " served to conjure up an image of the absurd *embrôisement* theory. As a result preformationism gradually diminished during the middle half of the eighteenth century, and its death blow was finally caused by Wolff who, in 1768, showed how the chick intestine is actually produced. After that epigenesis came to be accepted again by nearly all biologists.

Yet to-day, after a long lapse of time, there is no doubt that the preformationist was right. The attitude adopted by modern embryologists is well summarised by Huxley and de Beer[1], who remark that we are now vigorously preformationist as regards heredity, but rigorously epigenetic as regards embryological development. Preformationism, in fact, was not a theory which could help forward the descriptive study of embryology. Not until our own day, when genetical studies have revealed the fact that heredity is caused by genes and chromosomes, has its essential truth been rediscovered.

As yet, the victory of preformationism, though certain, is not complete, for the outlook in embryology is still epigenetic. Yet no one to-day doubts that this is only because our knowledge is still so limited. The gap between the genes and the developing embryo has not yet been bridged; we still do not know how it is that the highly complex molecules of nucleo-proteins, out of which the genes are constructed, are able to build up limbs and brains and eyes. When this knowledge is available—it will not be for a long time yet —embryology will be in a position to start at the beginning with the gene, instead of at that arbitrary point at which the microscope first brings structures into view.

When this time comes, science will have returned completely to the old preformationist view, almost in the form that Malpighi taught it. For Malpighi did not believe that minute men and women, with tiny pre-formed eyes and stomachs of the correct relative sizes were present inside his eggs, but merely that eggs contained parts corresponding to all the final structures.

* * * *

Having completed this brief survey of the old controversies between the rival views of the early embryologists, it remains for us to assess them in the light of the much clearer outlook which we possess to-day.

The first point of importance is one which has been largely overlooked by modern historians of science—it is the interconnection which has always existed between the

[1] J. S. Huxley and G. R. de Beer, *The Elements of Experimental Embryology*, 1934, p. 2.

physical and biological sciences. The physical science of the seventeenth century was essentially atomistic, and for this reason it was impossible for biologists to develop the doctrine of preformationism at that time. For preformationism, at least in its cruder forms, involved the idea that matter could be subdivided indefinitely, so that there was nothing ridiculous in supposing that parts of animals could be built up out of matter on any scale, however small.

In the following century atomism declined—Laplace was, indeed, able to show that the only good argument which Newton had been able to develop for the existence of atoms, an argument based upon the velocity of sound, was completely fallacious. The way was, therefore, open for scientists and philosophers to believe that matter could be subdivided indefinitely. It was this fact that opened the door, not only to preformationism (which could, after all, be made to tally with atomism, provided that atoms were sufficiently small), but to the encasement theory. It was, as we have seen, this belief in the non-existence of atoms to which Malebranche appealed in his argument for encasement. Even at a considerably later date we find Buffon[1] frankly admitting that " as matter is infinitely divisible, this gradual diminition of size is not impossible," despite the fact that he was a strong opponent of encasement.

Towards the end of the eighteenth century, the position changed. Although Dalton had not as yet conducted his classical researches of the first few years of the nineteenth century, a feeling was nevertheless gaining ground that, whatever mathematicians might say, atoms existed none the less. Thus, in 1794 we find Erasmus Darwin[2] arguing against preformation on the ground that this view " ascribes a greater tenuity to organized matter than we can readily admit ; as these included embryos are supposed each of them to consist of the various and complicated parts of

[1] *Natural History*, Eng. Ed. of 1785, II, p. 138.
[2] *Zoonomia*, 1724, I, p. 490.

animal bodies." He continues by arguing that, if preformation is right, atoms would need to be smaller than
the devils who tempted St. Anthony, each of which, so
the schoolmen said, was so small that twenty thousand of
them could " dance on the point of the finest needle without incommoding each other." This, thought Darwin,
was ridiculous. In point of fact, it is an understatement.

Thus, epigenesis finally came to be accepted largely because
the physical sciences of the day made it impossible any
longer to believe in the existence of exceedingly small animals,
coiled up inside their parents. Indeed, the later development
of the encasement theory seemed clearly to require that these
little homunculi would have to be much smaller than the
atoms themselves. In the end, therefore, epigenesis, being
the only rival, won an easy victory over preformationism.

    *   *   *   *   *

Secondly, the history of embryology illustrates another
extraordinarily important point. It shows us how a
basically false theory can replace a basically true one.

In accepting epigenesis, biologists, for the time being,
gave up all hope of understanding how eggs turned into
animals. And well they might. The people of that day
possessed not the remotest conception of the complexity
inherent in life. Even to-day, after centuries of effort, we
are only beginning, not so much to solve the problems of
life, as to learn in what those problems consist.

However, if it explained nothing, epigenesis at least left the
ground free. Biologists ceased to be tempted to fancy that
they could see adult forms in eggs, and they set themselves to
the task of compiling reliable information, upon which a later
generation might one day place an interpretation. In this
way epigenesis acted as a stimulus to scientific advance.

Situations of this kind are well known in the history of
science. A basically false theory (Kekulé's theory that all
atoms have constant valencies, for example) is sometimes
accepted enthusiastically because it leads to further advance,

while a basically true theory (e.g. Frankland's theory that valency could vary) is rejected because it is unfruitful.

It was the same in the history of embryology. Preformation had asserted that the elaborate organisation of an animal could not arise *de novo* : it must be caused by an underlying microscopic or sub-microscopic structure. As Meyer points out, the objection of Charles Bonnet (one of the greatest of the preformationists, who lived 1720–1793) to epigenesis was apparently " that of those of the present day who reject the idea of spontaneous generation implied in the doctrine of evolution ; for the epigenesists of his day did, in fact, assume that each generation arose anew from unorganized substances at the time of conception."[1]   Nevertheless, preformationism was rejected because it did nothing to stimulate accurate research, for the naturalists of that day were not in a position to see, far less to appreciate, the significance of the chromosome.   As a result, it became the custom for several generations of the writers of text-books, who hardly ever paused to consider the basic principles involved, to pour mocking scorn and abuse upon preformationism in all its forms.

We see, therefore, that preformationism was an attempt to treat embryology scientifically, while epigenesis rested upon vitalistic or quasi-magical interpretations of nature. This view is supported by the fact that those epigenesists, who upheld the doctrine at the time when preformation was the fashion, tended to have marked vitalistic sympathies.   Though there are one or two notable exceptions[2] it is still true that for most of them " the conception of epigenesis, at any rate to begin with, is invariably connected with the conviction of the reality of spontaneous generation."[3]   Thus, one of the best known opponents of preformation was John Turberville Needham, who, as we have seen, was a vigorous supporter of spontaneous

---

[1] A. W. Meyer, *The Rise of Embryology*, 1939, p. 81.
[2] J. Needham, *A History of Embryology*, 1934, pp. 187, 191.
[3] H. Driesch, *The History and Theory of Vitalism*, 1914, p. 39.

generation.   Believing, as he did, in the spontaneous generation of entire organisms, he naturally felt no difficulty in supposing that spontaneous generation also took place in eggs.

*   *   *   *   *

Thirdly, we have to consider the relation of embryology
to evolution.   By now the importance of the history of
embryology to the subject matter of this book will probably
have become obvious.   The subjects—embryology and
evolution—are intertwined at every stage in their development.   There is scarcely a theory of the one that has not
its counterpart in the other.   The theory of recapitulation
—the theory that the various stages in the growth of the
embryo recapitulate the various stages in the evolutionary
history of the race—makes the connexion closer still.

In the case of evolution, as in the case of embryology,
the fundamental question is the same : How did it come
about that highly ordered structures came to exist ?   Were
they produced spontaneously by a self-ordering principle
at work in nature ?   Or were they already present in a
form too small to be seen by the naked eye ?

Preformationists said that the structures were already
present in the original cells and were capable of development when conditions were right.   In its essentials this
view was correct, but, instead of examining nature with an
open mind, many believers allowed their fancies to get
the better of them.   It was for this reason that preformationism had to be destroyed before science could progress.
As a result, epigenesis, equivalent to a kind of spontaneous
generation within an amorphous cell repeated at each
generation, became the popular view until recent years.

Controversies concerning the history of the race developed along closely similar lines.   There were those who
claimed that the forces of nature, being blind, could never
create the complex organization of a higher animal.   The
solution, they said, must be found in original creations of
the various species, or at least of some of them.   Or else,

if ever the scientific evidence should positively demand a rising complexity as a fact of pre-history, then it would be necessary to suppose that very complex but *apparently* simple creatures had been created at the first, but that during the course of ages the real complexities latent within them had become revealed (orthogenesis). Here we have a parallel to preformationism. On the other hand, there were the materialistic evolutionists who, like the spontaneous generationists of a bygone day, simply did not know how it had all happened, but were content to imagine that natural forces were in the habit of doing wonderful things. In them we see a parallel to the epigenesists.

The analogy may be developed yet further. The effects upon science of the two pairs of rival schools were closely similar. Like its preformationist counterpart, the doctrine of special creation was highly injurious to science. Well-known naturalists frankly admitted that they thought it was unwise to investigate certain groups of organisms for fear that the special creation theory might be undermined. Fossils were explained away and their connexion with later forms denied, anatomical resemblances between different species, the presence of vestigial organs and so on, were overlooked or regarded as of no importance. Serious research was at a standstill.

In time special creation, like preformationism before it, was abandoned. And here again, the result was beneficial to science. Biological research was provided with a co-ordinating idea and progressed rapidly. But evolution did little or nothing to provide a positive alternative to special creation. Darwin claimed that when once nature had created variations, the more favourable ones would be retained by natural selection, but he did not know how the variations were caused in the first place. Nor, as we shall see in the sequel, has modern knowledge been any more successful in explaining how natural forces can be creative of novelty.

As for the end of the story, that must be left to the sequel.

CHAPTER III

BEFORE DARWIN

IN ANCIENT TIMES, WHEN SPONTANEOUS GENERATION AND wholesale transformations were the accepted order of the day, there was little incentive to discuss whether or not species could slowly change into one another throughout the course of long periods of history. The greater miracle happened every day ; what need was there to look for the lesser ?

It was probably for this reason that Aristotle never expressed himself clearly on the issue of evolution. And for a long time after him, too, evolution remained a matter of academic interest, much less important than the more rapid generations and transformations that nature revealed on every hand.

Yet the rigidity of species formed no part of the doctrine of the Middle Ages. It was commonly supposed that, according to the Bible, the black, yellow and white races of mankind were all descended from Adam. It followed that changes in the colour of the skin must therefore have taken place within historic times. In the Bible there was also the familiar story of how, after Jacob had put striped poplar in front of Laban's flocks, the offspring were striped and speckled and presumably bred true to type. Thus, it was clear to all that variations occurred. Indeed, we find St. Augustine writing quite naturally of those creatures which " being removed by degrees in time and space make and unmake beautiful variations."

Similar statements of evolutionary, or quasi-evolutionary, views are doubtless to be found in thousands scattered, almost at random, throughout the rather inaccessible literature of the Middle Ages. The subject never, at any time became a burning topic of the day, yet quite advanced evolutionary views seem often to have been held, without being considered particularly heterodox. A case in point is that of Job of Edessa (ninth century), for whom, as Mingana remarks : " the real fact of the creation is to be conceived in the notion that God created the simple elements and allowed them to carry out the complicated work of building up the creation with its innumerable genera and species."[1] Job was a devout Christian, of Nestorian persuasion.

Passing over the centuries, we learn that Henry of Hesse (1325–1397)—a strong believer in spontaneous generation, who was also inclined to believe that foxes were generated from the carcasses of dead dogs—boldly expressed doubts as to whether the various kinds of dogs, horses and even men, really belonged to the same species. Hesse was sceptical of the claims of the astrologers of his day and was inclined to belittle the influence of the stars upon men as individuals. He seems to have thought, however, that by exerting their influence upon animals over long periods of time, the stars had the power to form new species from old.

Later, Jacob Sylvius (1478–1555), one of the greatest anatomists of his day, argued that since the structure of the human body did not altogether agree with the description of it given by Galen, man's body must have changed since Galen's day—a remarkable rate of evolution as judged by modern ideas !

Equally interesting were the views of Buteo (1559) and the Calvinist Lambert Daneau (*Christian Physics*, 1575), both of whom argued that terrestrial animals might once have comprised but thirty genera, so that Noah would not have been faced with an impossible task when he took them into the ark.[2]

[1] *Book of Treasures.* Trans. A. Mingana, p. xxviii.
[2] However, L. Thorndike (*History of Magic and Experimental Science*, Vol. IV, p. 347) points out that Buteo and Daneau *may* not have had the idea of evolution specifically in view, since they *may* have supposed that God later did another miracle by increasing the number of genera after the Flood.

Other better known writers might also be quoted. Bacon (seventeenth century) says, " that plants sometimes degenerate to the point of changing into other plants." Leibnitz, speaking of the *Ammonites*, remarks : " It is credible that by means of such great changes (of habitat) even the species of animals are often changed." Indeed, scores of the old writers make similar remarks. In our day they have had their works examined to see whether they enshrine the precious gem of evolutionary thought and have been judged accordingly ; the fact is too often overlooked that the possibility of transformism of species was at one time almost a commonplace idea.

Thus, it is clear that the doctrine of the fixity of species was no part of the intellectual climate of the Middle Ages, and far less was it an article of Christian faith. The most widely held theory on the subject was that of " degeneration "— a word which had not its modern meaning, but corresponded rather closely with what we, to-day, mean by " mutation."[1]   In other words, changes were supposed to occur, so that offspring no longer resembled their parents. There was, of course, no suggestion that each succeeding generation became more complex than the one before ; that " degeneration " involved a gradual ascent in an evolutionary scale.   At the same time it did not *necessarily* involve a descent, though this was often the case, for a species might sometimes die out or become less fitted to live.

*   *   *   *   *

We have now to consider the effect upon the doctrine of evolution of the new knowledge which ushered in the modern era.

In Europe the sixteenth and seventeenth centuries brought with them an age of rumour, enlightenment and enthusiasm such as had never been paralleled in any previous time.   During the long Middle Ages, scholars had been inclined to smile at the strange stories of other lands

[1] See C. Zirkle, *American Naturalist*, 1935, **69**, 417.

that were contained in the classical writings.   Now, however, with the discovery of the new world and the dawning
of an age of travel, they were disposed to think again.
Strange tales coming from the ends of the earth, began to
circulate in wild profusion.   Rumours of powerful Eastern
magicians and alchemists, of the wonderful bezoar stones,
of new sea-monsters, of insects that shone so brightly in
the dark that natives used them instead of candles, of
skiapodes and of many another wonder began to tingle
the ears and stir the hearts of men and of women.

Tales of ever-burning lamps, of live toads totally enclosed in rocks, filled the air.   Above all, there was constant
fear of the anti-Christ.   In 1599 a rumour circulated everywhere to the effect that the Man of Sin had been born in
Babylon.   Jews were hurrying to receive him as their
Messiah.   Months had hardly passed when another rumour
spread to the effect that he had been conceived by Satan
in Paris.   A witch had confessed that she had rocked the
infant anti-Christ to sleep on her knees—he had claws on
his feet, he wore no shoes and he spoke all languages !

The world was full of marvels.   There was an air of
expectancy.   None could guess what the next marvel
might be.   And science, then in its early years, had already
begun to bring surprises.   The telescope was revealing
new planets, new moons, new stars ; men were speculating
wildly about the inhabitants of these celestial orbs.   Micro-
scopes revealed a new and hitherto unknown world of the
very small.   The time seemed ripe for a huge advance in
knowledge if only men could cast their foolish prejudices
aside and look for truth in God's other book—the book
of nature.   Who knew whether, with the help of God,
science might bring in an age of prosperity and happiness
hitherto undreamed of ?

Historians of science tell us that as these new and wonderful ideas circulated from mouth to mouth and from land
to land, they had the result of diminishing critical judgment

throughout Europe. Superstitions that had been dead
for ages, or kept alive only by the few, now spread like
wild-fire. It was more difficult than ever to distinguish
the true from the false.

For generations scholars had made fun of the monstrous
men mentioned in the stories of Pliny, and of the assertion
of such writers as Ctesias that exceedingly small pigmies
existed in hot climes. Now it seemed possible, at least,
that such beings might really exist. Indeed, monkeys and
apes—small man-like creatures—were brought to Europe
for the first time. Patagonian giants had recently been
reported and, stranger still, negroes with lips hanging down
to their breasts. There was even the tale of an Eastern
patriarch who was 335 years old when the Portuguese
visited him in 1535. One of the many ideas that flourished
in the new mental atmosphere was that of alchemy—
alchemy not only in the narrow sense of turning base metals
into gold, but alchemy in all its phases—universal alchemy.

There is no space here to re-tell the stories of those
mysterious men who visited the savants of Europe, artfully
leaving behind them specimens of the Philosopher's Stone,
converting the most sceptical minds of the age to belief in
alchemy. That, as we have said, was but one side of the
story. On the other, the wonderful transformations that
God allowed with metals, He allowed also with animals
and plants. Indeed, the distinction was hardly worth
drawing in those days, for the metals themselves were
supposed to be derived from a living tree which grew with
its roots embedded in the centre of the earth. Its branches
were the mineral veins. They grew slowly, just like those
of any other tree, so that when once a mine had been ex-
hausted it was only necessary to close it until the tree had
sprouted new shoots once more. And it was supposed
that just as twigs and wood turned into foliage so, by the
secret alchemy of this wonder-working tree, the base
minerals turned into rarer ones—lead and mercury into silver

and gold.   The alchemist of metals sought only to hasten a process which nature accomplished in thousands of years.

With this background of thought, it was not unreasonable to believe that barnacles turned into geese (as an Irish clergyman so steadfastly affirmed—for had he not seen the geese fly away ?), that basilisks hatched out eggs laid by cocks or that in the year 1553 a woman had given birth to a frog with the tail of a snake. Aldrovandi, the greatest writer on natural history in his day, was disposed to doubt these stories, but many believed them.   In any case it was not clear how such events differed from many other changes that took place in nature, about which there was no manner of doubt.   As Sir Isaac Newton himself remarked, nature " seems delighted with Transmutations. . . .   Eggs grow from insensible Magnitudes, and change into Animals ; Tadpoles into Frogs ; and Worms into flies."[1]   Sir Isaac continued by asking whether even light and matter might not be interchangeable.   Nature's transformations were, in fact, so strange and so startling that there was no telling what would be reported next.

In such an age of speculation and wonder, it is no cause for surprise that a steady flow of incoming anecdotal stories about monkeys, baboons and orang-outangs began to make men wonder what the relation of these animals to men might be.   The problem of the native races was also of the deepest interest.   Giants and pigmies ; blacks, yellows and whites —were all descendants of Adam and Eve ?   The problem that had arisen only spasmodically during the Middle Ages now took on a new interest.   The feeling grew that the solution offered by the writers of the Middle Ages was correct.   To quote Francis Bacon : " It would be very difficult to generate new species, but less so to vary known species, and thus to produce many rare and unusual results."[2]

Then, slowly but surely, reaction set in.   As investigation proceeded, as the foundations of one science after another

[1] *Optics*, 1931 ed., p. 374.   [2] *Novum Organum*, 1620.   Bk. II, sect. 29.

were laid, it turned out that the transformations of nature were neither so numerous nor so startling as had been supposed. This was particularly the case in chemistry. The idea of the transmutation of the elements turned out to have been a big mistake. The long established belief that the wood and leaves of trees were but modified forms of water turned out to be false ; congealed ice did not turn to crystal (quartz) ; minerals in the earth retained their identity and the Philosopher's Stone itself fell into disrepute.

Even when all outward appearances suggested that a fundamental change had taken place, chemists were discovering that such was not really the case. Fire, destroyer of all things, left the elements quite unscathed—the carbon and hydrogen of wood were to be found unchanged in amount after combustion had taken place. To cap it all, both spontaneous generation and the doctrine that parents could produce progeny of a wholly unrelated kind, came to be seriously challenged. As science advanced, even the age-old belief that drops of water could turn into little green frogs had to be abandoned. And so it was that, one by one, the amazing transformations of nature turned out, for the most part, to be mythical.

In this way, as a result of the steady advance of science from the sixteenth to the eighteenth centuries, the whole face of nature began to change. In place of the unpredictable, the extraordinary, there came a sense that the world was governed by natural law ; that nature was tidy and that the human mind was capable of understanding the order and harmony that prevailed on every hand.

So the old unlimited transformism simply disappeared. There were limits to what could happen—limits that were determined by the unalterable laws of nature. The different kinds of material out of which the world was made had had their individuality stamped upon them at the creation and would remain unchanged for all time ; they could not be interconverted. Light and matter were distinct. Gravitational, electrical, magnetic and dynamical forces were not to be confused.

These views, which by the eighteenth century had come to form the background of scientific thought, were bound to have their effects upon biology. For in those days, men of science were not the narrow specialists that they so often are to-day ; one and all read widely and sought to co-ordinate their knowledge. So then, since in the physical sciences large scale transformations had turned out to be unreal, it was obviously worth investigating whether the same might not be true in biology.

The first results of such investigation showed at once that biology fell into line with physical science. Careful observation of animals and plants showed that they bred true to type. Very occasionally, of course, changes occurred, as in the formation of monsters. But again, observation showed that such creatures were not capable of reproducing their kind.

It was as a result of these considerations and observations that, for the first time in history, the doctrine of the fixity of species was propounded.

We meet it to begin with in the seventeenth century in the writings of John Ray, but it was not until the following century that it became widely accepted.

In the eighteenth century, Linnaeus (1707-1778), the great systematizer of zoology, became profoundly convinced that species were immutable. His belief, founded upon direct observation, was unshaken by the anatomical resemblances which he so frequently found to exist between different animals. " There are," he claimed " just so many species as in the beginning the Infinite Being created." Later Cuvier (1769–1832) who was the first to propound the idea of a genealogical tree in zoology, saw the relationships between animals even more clearly than had Linnaeus, but stoutly denied that the resemblances were due to any kind of physical relationship, but were rather due to the

Creator's plan.   God, he said, showed His skill in varying
the details while retaining the essentials.

Thus, by the beginning of the nineteenth century, at the
very time when Dalton was establishing the existence of the
chemical atoms—just so many kinds of them as in the beginning the Infinite Being had created—biologists too had come
to believe in the absolute fixity of species.   Followers
of Cuvier carried the doctrine to its logical extreme.
Many leading scientists—d'Orbigny, d'Archaiac, Barrande,
Forbes, Agassiz and others—carried the doctrine far further
than Cuvier had ever done.   The claim was even made
that the different races of mankind did not consist of a
single species, but of some sixty species, each of which
had been specially created.

In 1800 there was published in London the second part
of Edward King's *Morsels of Criticism*, in which he showed
how such views could be reconciled with the teaching of
the Bible.   Adam belonged to a superior race, the head
class or species of man.   Noah and his family were the only
representatives of Adam's species to have been preserved
in the deluge, which was not universal, and did not affect
the other human races.   What was true of man was also
true of the animals.   They too had been created in many
varieties, or species, and only the head or representative
species of each kind went with Noah into the ark.

Views of a kind similar to those of King had been propounded by Paracelsus in 1520 and by the Calvinist Isaac
de la Payrène in 1655.   The latter claimed that the black
races of mankind had been created together with the animals
on the sixth day of creation, but his views were very soon
branded as heretical.   It was King, whose books were a
veritable mine of scientific, linguistic and theological learning, who once again brought the polygenic theory of man's
origin to the fore.   And a dangerous doctrine it was too—
one that fitted in exactly with the prejudices of racial fanatics
and of those who sought to oppose the abolition of the slave

trade. In his infamous work, *The Inequality of Human Races*, published in French in 1854, Gobineau interpreted Genesis as King had done. Only now, of course, Adam became the ancestor of the *white* race, whose duty it was to rule the blacks and the yellows. Later H. S. Chamberlain, whose writings so greatly influenced Hitler, was to narrow the master-race still further and identify it with the Aryans.

Thus the older views of biologists, according to which animals by no means always bred true to type, became slowly replaced by the narrow dogma that species are immutable. And this doctrine itself was later carried to absurd limits. Yet in this flux of thought, biology was not alone. As we have already noted, an almost identical change of opinion took place in the physical sciences. Here also, until the seventeenth century, there had probably never been any suggestion that the different principles involved in physics were fundamentally distinct. For Newton, as we have seen, there was no difficulty in supposing that light and matter might be interchangeable. Indeed, he was inclined to think that light consisted of particles which were, presumably, like any other kind of matter. Other natural philosophers of the time thought along similar lines. Thus, for Robert Boyle even the different kinds of atoms were not fundamentally distinct, for he claimed that in theory at least, they could be turned into one another.

In the eighteenth century all these views were abandoned. Physics developed a number of distinct concepts. Length, mass, time, magnetism, electricity, gravitation, force, matter, energy and even heat (which in those days was supposed to be made of a special kind of matter—caloric) gradually came to be regarded as fundamentally distinct kinds of cosmic "stuff." In the early days of the nineteenth century, this tendency to lose the sense of unity in nature, reached absurd limits in chemistry. It was seriously supposed that even the chemical elements represented fundamentally different kinds of matter, all of them completely unconnected with one another.

It was obvious that such views prepared the way for reaction. Faraday, who did so much to break down the old barriers between the fundamental ideas of physics, was imbued, as he tells us, with a passionate longing to find unity in phenomena that were apparently unconnected. In the middle decades of the nineteenth century enormous strides were made in this direction—one of the greatest unifications of all being the discovery that energy could manifest itself in many different forms—as heat, light, electricity, kinetic and potential energy, chemically stored energy, etc.

It was inevitable that biologists, also, would turn to their own subject, to see whether similar unifications could not be made there also. The very extremism of the advocates of the fixity of species set the stage for reaction.

*   *   *   *   *

Standing aside from the ideas that are currently received in any period of history, there are always to be found certain writers and thinkers who attempt to spread their own unorthodox beliefs. While they are alive, they are generally looked upon as " cranks," or at least as " a bit queer," but when (if it ever happens) their views become accepted as a part of the general heritage of thought, posterity shouts their praises and announces that they were born before their time.

It was not otherwise in the case of evolution, a doctrine that had been held by many before Darwin's day. It is doubtful, in fact, if Darwin had anything really new to say about it, save for the mass of evidence with which he supported his claims.

We shall close this chapter by mentioning some of the more interesting of the precursors of Darwin.

At the end of the seventeenth century Edward Tyson [1] was convinced that man and ape had something at least in common. He had seen, so he tells us, an orang-outang in the Straits of Molucca (Malacca) : " It marches naturally

[1] E. Tyson, *Orang-Outang Sive Homo Sylvestris or the Anatomy of the Pigmie*, 1699. By orang-outang Tyson meant chimpanzee—the two animals were often confused in those days.

upon its two hind Feet, it makes use of its two arms as we do . . . it cries exactly like a child ; the whole outward action is so humane . . . that dumb men can scarce express better their conceptions and appetites."

The resemblance of this animal to man slowly implanted in Tyson's mind the idea that connexions existed between species of every kind. The wildest of the evolutionists of later days could not have given better expression to his conviction that no unbridgeable gulfs were to be found in nature. " From minerals to plants, from plants to animals ; and from animals to men ; the transition is so gradual, that there appears a very great similitude, as well between the meanest plant and some animals ; as between the lowest rank of men, and the highest of animals."

Tyson went on to argue that men and apes were so alike that they had been confused by the ancients. The little pigmies described by ancient writers were not, in fact, men at all, but monkeys—though from Tyson's point of view the difference was not, perhaps, so very important.

Before many years had passed by, the air was astir with tales of Peter the Wild Boy. This youth, so the story went, had been caught by George I in 1725 when his Majesty had been hunting in the woods near Hamelin in Germany. Rumour insisted that the boy could use his limbs so adroitly that no squirrel could compete with him in tree-climbing ; indeed, had the tree on which he was perching not been sawn from beneath him, he would never have been caught at all. After capture he had escaped from Hanover and returned to the forests a second time. Recaptured, he was brought to England, there to be presented at Court in 1726, when he was granted a pension for life and entrusted to Dr. Arbuthnot, a well-known physician of the time, whose duty it was to teach him to talk.

Peter—so the story went—was especially fond of raw flesh and bones. He would run seventy or eighty miles a day. His left hand was partly webbed. If provoked he would run after those who teased him " making a strange noise." Periodically he tore his bedclothes to shreds. He was rumoured to know the language of animals and to have been deeply offended on one occasion when he neighed to a horse but obtained no reply.[1]

James Burnet, later Lord Monboddo (1714–1799) studied Peter with great diligence. In the portly volumes of his *Ancient Metaphysics* he had much to say about the Wild Boy. Here and in his *Origins and Progress of Language*, he discoursed at length on the relationship between men and apes. He asserted, on the authority of Buffon, that women might safely mate with orang-outangs and produce children more healthy than British boys and girls. One such child was so robust that it " ran about as soon as it was born." Since inter-breeding was possible, it was clear that apes and men were nearly related and this relationship showed itself also in habits—for orangs buried their dead with care and devotion.

In Peter, his Lordship saw the very embodiment of his theories. Peter was the true missing link. Men could talk, apes could not, while Peter, despite years of education at a school in Hertfordshire, was able to speak only an odd word or two, he " had only learned to articulate his own name *Peter* and the name of *King George*. It was clear that Peter was a borderline case. There was however one outstanding difficulty. Peter was not adorned even with the vestige of a tail. It is said that his lordship solved the difficulty in a startling way. By searching in the dustbins around hospitals, he often found objects (umbilical cords) that bore a suspicious resemblance to tails. Rumour has it that he eventually became convinced that all children are born with tails, but that, as a result of a joint conspiracy among midwives, these were always discreetly removed at birth, so that the public might never accept his lordship's views.

[1] See Dean Swift's delightful satire, *It cannot Rain but it Pours* or *London strow'd with Rarities*, 1726.

The small difficulty occasioned by the difference in gait between animals and men was solved by Monboddo in a similar manner. Two children in Devonshire, so he says, were sent out by their mother to run wild and they immediately ran on all fours with great celerity. These and other examples, says his lordship, prove " beyond doubt, that the natural motion of man is upon all fours."

Wild men continued to appear periodically. In 1802 one was found in the woods of Lacaune. It seemed to be about a dozen years old. It would not eat bread but liked potatoes, preferably boiled. " If suffered to go near a tree," we read, " it climbs with great quickness. It laughs in a very agreeable manner ; and, when robbed of its potatoes, sends forth a shrill cry." Most wonderful of all it could survive the coldest winters, though it lived quite naked in the forests.[1]

While the idea that men and apes were connected with one another was kept alive by the periodic appearance of wild men, a certain number of naturalists and other writers rebelled against the generally accepted views. Buffon (1753–1778), who had been orthodox at first, later came to believe that at least some new species had arisen by alteration from a primitive stock. Lamarck, too, developed his theory of use-inheritance (often called the theory of inherit ance of acquired characters) according to which an animal could hand on to its progeny habits, skills and changes in bodily organs which it had acquired during life as a result of use. In this way and over long intervals of time, so he claimed, the various species had undergone profound changes. Thus, he explained the existence of snakes by saying that lizard-like creatures at one time developed the habit of persistently crawling through holes, as a result of which their legs disappeared and their bodies became yet longer. Or again, giraffes came into being in the

[1] British Critic, 1802, **20**, 160.

manner so elegantly described in later years by Lord Neaves:

> " *A deer with a neck that was longer by half*
>   *Than the rest of its family's (try not to laugh)*
> *By stretching and stretching, became a Giraffe*
>   *Which nobody can deny.*"

At the end of the eighteenth century, Erasmus Darwin, grandfather of Charles, revealed himself to be an ardent evolutionist. " Eat or be eaten," was, he claimed, the first law of nature and it was one that he often mentioned at the dinner table. In his *Temple of Nature* he sought to show how this law would lead to an " improving excellence " in every part of creation. The favoured ones remaining after " hunger, war and pestilence, disease and death had swept the superfluous myriads from the earth " would improve from one generation to another :

> " *These as successive generations bloom.*
> *New powers acquire, and larger limbs assume ;*
> *Whence countless groups of vegetation spring,*
> *And breathing realms of fin, and feet, and wing.*"

Another well known writer was Diderot, in France, who, like Erasmus Darwin, stated the principle of natural selection quite clearly : " I maintain . . . that the monsters annihilated one another in succession, that all faulty combinations of matter disappeared, and that only those survived whose mechanisms implied no important misadaptation, and who had the power of supporting and perpetuating themselves."

In the early nineteenth century, evolution made further headway. In 1813, W. C. Wells suggested that natural selection would account for the dark colour of native races.

In 1831 the house of Longmans, in London, published Patrick Matthew's work, *On Naval Timber and Arboriculture*. Not until later days did this book attract attention among biologists, yet it contained as clear a statement on the principle of natural selection as Charles Darwin himself could have written : " As Nature . . . has a power of increase far beyond what is needed to supply the place of what falls by Time's decay, those individuals who possess not the requisite strength . . . fall prematurely without reproducing . . . their place being occupied by the more perfect of their own kind."

Another landmark in the history of evolution was set up in 1844, when an anonymous book appeared called *Vestiges of the Natural History of Creation*. It had been written by Robert Chambers, editor of *Chambers's Journal*, but elaborate precautions had been taken to preserve its anonymity. In the catalogue of the British Museum it stood, at various times, under numerous names, and not until the twelfth edition was the authorship acknowledged.

The tone of this book was openly evolutionary, though devoutly Christian. According to the author, a universal law of nature was for ever creating order out of chaos. Chaotic matter in the heavens condensed to give orderly worlds, where highly complex organisms developed. " We see a gradual evolution of high from low, of complicated from simple, of special from general, all in unvarying order, and therefore all natural, although all of divine ordination." Again, in " the decreeing of laws to bring the whole about was an act involving such a degree of wisdom and device as we can only attribute, adoringly, to the one Eternal and Unchangeable."

Most of the arguments later used by the evolutionary school were employed by Chambers. Even recapitulation was taught in no uncertain manner. " The frog, for some time after its birth, is a fish with external gills . . . nor is man himself exempt from this law. His first form is that which is permanent in the animalcule. His organisa-tion gradually passes through conditions generally resembl-ing a fish, a reptile, a bird, and the lowest mammalia, before it attains its specific maturity," and, the author went on to say, at one stage the growing human embryo was like the ape. Chambers also raised the question as to whether man had reached the summit of his evolutionary career. He suggested that, in time, a species greatly superior to modern man might arise.

The book produced a storm of controversy. It was referred to with admiring words in the House of Commons. Writers and reviewers were sometimes sycophantic in their praise, sometimes violently critical.

Tait's Edinburgh Magazine claimed that the evolutionary outlook agreed well with the Mosaic record, but urged that the new view was not scientifically acceptable. *The Christian Reformer*—a Unitarian publication—was highly critical, chiefly on the ground that the author had assumed that scientific " laws " operated apart from God.

Blackwood's Magazine (April, 1845) ridiculed the whole idea (see later, p. 175)—but without theological prejudice. *The Christian Examiner* (1846), of Boston, pointed out that the attitude of the book was very similar to that of Cudworth. The difficulty was that the unknown author seemed to be a determinist, but if his evolutionary ideas were right, religion would be unaffected. *The British Magazine* said the book was mischievous and pointed out that scientists condemned it. *The Intellectual Repository* (1845) thought it made God too far off—as Creator only. *The Church of England Quarterly Review* (1845) remarked : " A more infidel or a more stupid publication has rarely appeared . . . it is inconsistent even with the heathen ideas of a God." *The Examiner* (November, 1844)—a Sunday paper—was highly favourable. The new view was said to be entirely consistent with Christianity. The writer, who was clearly very religious, could not " too earnestly recommend it to the attention of thoughtful men. It is," he said, " the first attempt that has been made to connect the natural sciences into a history of creation."

And so the controversy raged. In the end opinion settled down unfavourably towards the book. In November, 1845, the *Athenæum* devoted space to a short summary of the replies that had been written to it. The upshot was that astronomers condemned it—Sir John Herschell said, "there are no traces of chaos in the heavens." And philosophers condemned it also, for they said that the author has mistaken the operation of a law for the discovery of a cause.

In July, 1845, there appeared in the *Edinburgh Review* an outspoken attack on the *Vestiges* written by Sedgwick, the Cambridge geologist, who claimed—not without reason—to be speaking for the scientists of the country. "All in the book is shallow; and all is second-hand . . . sober truth and sober nonsense, strangely blended." "We venture to affirm that no man who has any name in science, properly so-called . . . has spoken well of the book, or regarded it with any feelings but those of deep aversion. We say this advisedly, after exchanging thoughts with some of the best-informed men in Britain." Again, no religious prejudice was invoked. Sedgwick's strictures were in the main sound—and would be considered so to-day.

So in time the *Vestiges* was almost forgotten by the scientific world. But it had a deep and lasting effect on the mind of the public, preparing them for the evolutionary views that were later to be promulgated. Tennyson's *In Memoriam*, published in 1850, with its idea of nature "red in tooth and claw" and natural selection so intense, that "of myriad seeds she often brings but one to bear," helped to keep the evolutionary idea alive. So also, though at the time far less influential, did the early writings of Herbert Spencer. Such influences were not without effect on Darwin himself, who read the *Vestiges* soon after it was published and was very favourably impressed.

Thus the first all-embracing evolutionary theory presented to the public came, not from an atheist, but from a Christian. Nor was its rejection due to theology, but to the science of the day. These are facts which those who believe in the myth that theology has always been at war with science, might well bear in mind.

CHAPTER IV

THE TRIUMPH OF EVOLUTION [1]

As the eighteenth century drew to its close, dreams of social improvement provided an unending topic of conversation up and down the country. The influence of Rousseau was beginning to make itself felt in England. Godwin, Condorcet and others were spreading the exciting news that the productive capacity of the community was now increasing by leaps and bounds, that there would soon be enough for all and that before long poverty might become a thing of the past.

Were such opinions soundly based? Or were they the ravings of irresponsible enthusiasts? This was one of the burning questions of the day. And, among the thousands who discussed it, were a father, Daniel Malthus by name, and his son Thomas. Daniel, the father, was a personal friend of Rousseau and an enthusiastic supporter of the new doctrines. Naturally enough he wished, if possible, to convince his son of their truth. In this he was at first successful, but Thomas soon began to be troubled by a difficulty. Speaking of the would-be reformers, he later wrote: " I have been warmed and delighted with the enchanting picture which they hold forth. I ardently wish for such happy improvements. But I see great, and to my understanding, unconquerable difficulties in the way of them."

The difficulty that Thomas Malthus felt was simply this.

[1] In this and the following chapter no attempt has been made to give detailed references to the quotations from Darwin's writings. Unless otherwise stated they may all be readily found in the standard sources (*Life and Letters of Charles Darwin*, 1887, and *More etters of Charles Darwin*, 1903, etc., etc.). For the best modern accounts of the Darwinian controversy see G. West, *Charles Darwin*, 1937, and C. E. Raven, *Science, Religion and the Future*, 1943.

If the standard of living of the poor was raised, they would inevitably increase in numbers until their standard was back at its old level. Since, according to the economists of the day, the population always increased more rapidly than the means of production, it was impossible for the latter to keep pace with the former. Men, therefore, were doomed to a " struggle for existence "—these were the very words that Malthus used—and their standard of living would always remain at the level at which life was only just possible.

With his father's encouragement, these views were in time enshrined in Thomas Malthus's *Essay on Population*, which, appearing first in 1798, had passed through six editions by 1826.

Academic as it was, this pessimistic doctrine was destined to exert a profound effect upon the future of the world. Indeed, it was soon welcomed by a section of the upper class, who saw in it more than sufficient ground for social lethargy. What motive could inspire them to ameliorate the conditions of the poor if, in the long run, their labour would only serve to increase the number of people who lived in squalor ? Later, others, seeing the hopelessness and indeed wickedness of such an attitude, sought for artificial means by which the outworking of the law of Malthus might be averted. Eugenics and the birth-control movement were of this character. But, to return to our subject, it was the Malthusian law which directly inspired the revival of the theory of evolution. " In October, 1838," Darwin tells us, " I happened to read for my amusement *Malthus on Population* and, being well prepared to appreciate the struggle for existence which everywhere goes on from long-continued observations of the habits of animals and plants, it at once struck me that under these circumstances favourable variations would tend to be preserved, and unfavourable ones to be destroyed. The result of this would be the formation of new species."

Wallace, who at a later date discovered evolution independently, also testified to the direct influence of Malthus.

*   *   *   *   *

Charles Darwin has formed the subject of innumerable biographies, memoirs and articles. Yet another detailed biography would serve no useful purpose, but there are a number of features of Darwin's life and work that are apt to be overlooked in the very abundance of the material that has become available. In the short account of Darwin that follows, we shall have cause to draw attention to some of them.

As a youth Charles Darwin was a ne'er-do-well. Unsuited to the rigorous classical training that was imposed upon him at Shrewsbury School, he was sent, in 1826, by his father, Dr. Robert Darwin, to Edinburgh University, where it was hoped that he would settle down quietly to his studies and qualify in due time as a medical practitioner. Though interested at first, Charles—convinced that he was going to inherit money enough to make him independent for life—became listless and bored and before long decided that he could no longer be bothered to study seriously. Robert Darwin, on the other hand, was determined that his son should not become an idle sporting man. Admonition proving useless, he brought Charles home and urged him to decide on a profession. Before long Charles began to toy with a suggestion that he should become a minister in the Church of England. He read theological books for a while and eventually decided that his convictions were sufficiently strong for him to proceed. With this end in view, his father sent him to Christ's College, Cambridge, in 1828.

Once at Cambridge, Charles wasted his time even more than he had done at Edinburgh. He rarely studied or even attended lectures, except for a few which were compulsory, while most of his time was spent with a clique of

riotous young men. We know little of his mental conflicts at this period, but they were certainly deep-seated
On one occasion, he had a very serious conversation with
a fellow undergraduate, who was also destined for the
Church. He asked his friend whether, at his coming
ordination, he could truthfully say that he had been
" inwardly moved by the Holy Spirit " to enter the ministry. His friend said that he could not. Whereupon
Charles said : " Neither can I and therefore I cannot take
orders." But such moments were few and far between.
It was not long before Charles had lulled his conscience
and returned once more to the life of pleasure in which
he still professed to be studying for Holy Orders.

Again, after seeing something of the pain that shooting
could give to the dumb creation, he vowed he would
never shoot again. But months had scarcely elapsed when,
as an act of rebellion against his father, he broke his vow.
Other conflicts, too, have been conjectured by the psycho-
analysts[1]. They are likely enough, but positive evidence
is lacking.

The relationship of Charles to his father was unfortunate
and mirrored his relationship to God. The life he was
living at Cambridge was clearly inconsistent with the sacred
calling to which he had pledged himself. Yet he could
not easily withdraw. Twice already he had failed to live
up to his father's expectations of him and it would have
been difficult to disappoint his father a third time. There
was also an additional difficulty. At Cambridge his im-
provident ways had brought with them a load of debt
which he was unable to pay off himself. For a while he
feared to tell his father, but in the end it came out and his
father paid the bill. It would not have been easy to tell
so generous a father that all the money he had spent on
his son's education had been wasted.

In the same way Charles' position as regards theological

[1] Notably by E. J. Kempf, *Psychopathology*, 1921.

beliefs was invidious. He no longer expected his father to leave him money unless he made good on his own account, and he now saw himself forced to make a living by serving God in the capacity of a minister of the Gospel. Though he had been honest enough in his first study of Christian books, it is probable enough that at a later stage he hardly dared to consider his doubts. For some time he was prepared to accept the creeds and the thirty-nine articles without questioning and was uncritically delighted when, after some years at Cambridge, he read Paley.

There are few records that Charles ever tried to pass on his religious beliefs to others. In 1829 he wrote a rather formal letter to his friend Fox, whose sister had died. In this he said that Fox doubtless knew of the " pure and holy comfort " afforded by the Bible, a comfort which would make anything that he might say of little moment. Later, when on the *Beagle*, he once rather naïvely quoted a text in the Bible to settle a point of morality, and was apparently surprised that he was laughed at by the sailors. Those are the only two stories showing even the least attempt, on the part of Charles, to share with others his Christian faith. It is not surprising that his convictions died : for he never seemed to have realized that convictions do not grow unless they are fed by action. Likely enough, Charles deliberately avoided reading much theology and permitted his interests to develop along other channels.

In 1831 Charles had completed the work necessary for his B.A. degree, but was required to remain two further terms in residence, though without the necessity of working for examinations. It was during this period that he became a close friend of Sedgwick and Henslow—friendships which soon opened the way to the next stage in his career.

*   *   *   *   *

Immediately after Darwin had graduated at Cambridge, in 1831, he had been urged to apply for the post of naturalist on board the *Beagle* which was about to sail on a surveying expedition. His application was successful. He sailed at the end of the year and did not return home until October, 1836, after which he never again left Great Britain.

While at Edinburgh, Charles Darwin had become familiar with the views of his grandfather, Dr. Erasmus Darwin, so that evolutionary teaching was by no means new to him. Again and again, during the course of the voyage, he had been struck by the evidences of evolution which nature seemed to provide. Sometimes he would find a fossil of an animal that did not exactly resemble the skeletons of animals indigenous to the area. Or again, he would notice that in a group of islands, each island had its own peculiar species, so specific that the natives themselves could tell from which island a given specimen had come. Occasionally, Charles discussed the possibility of evolution with FitzRoy, though without expressing himself dogmatically. It was during the voyage that Darwin resolved to collect evidence which might bear upon the point. It was not long before he was entirely convinced as to the truth of evolution, and the problem that lay before him now, was how best to present the evidence to the scientific world. The myth that Darwin took twenty years to make up his mind on the subject has long since been exploded.

On returning to England, Charles was offered the post of Secretaryship of the Geographical Society, a post which he held from 1838 to 1841. He married in 1840 and when, in 1841, his health had become so bad that he could no longer continue his work, he removed with his wife to Downe, where he lived until the end of his life.

As we have already seen, Darwin read Malthus in 1838, not long after his return to England, and it was then that he saw the significance of the idea of the " struggle for existence " in biology. He also read the *Vestiges* soon after its publication and was favourably impressed—but

the devastating criticism that this book received from the
scientific world, made him wonder more than ever how
he should set about his scheme for propounding essentially
the same doctrine. Again and again he broached the
subject with the scientific men of his day, and it became
more than ever clear to his mind that evolutionary views
were not going to be at all popular. He soon realized
that it was unwise to admit the nature of his beliefs even
to friends ; he merely allowed it to be known that he was
interested in collecting evidence that bore on the possibility
of mutability among species.

Darwin's indecision brought increasing mental strain.
He was jealous of his reputation and feared what contemporary scientists would say if he came out boldly as
an advocate of the mutability of species. He had every
reason to believe that his book, if ever he wrote one,
would be treated no less harshly than the *Vestiges*. Sometimes he thought that it would be wiser not to proceed
with the project at all. There was plenty of work to do
and, when he had finished work on his specimens, there
would be time enough to seek ordination in the Church.
But no sooner had he all but made up his mind accordingly,
than the conviction would come over him irresistibly that,
sooner or later *somebody* would enjoy the distinction for
the discovery of evolution. What a shame it would be if
that somebody stole his thunder.

Thus he vacillated, for month after month and year after
year. Of course he must write a book to prove his views.
But what kind of a book should it be ? Sometimes he
would start to write only to throw the results into the waste-
paper basket. When his mood was more favourable he
would set to work on a *short* book only to toy with the idea
that it must be a long one after all. Or again, he would
start a long book while half convinced that it ought to be
short. Unconsciously, procrastination was all he desired.
As with his theological convictions, so now with evolution,

his undue regard for the praise and blame of men made simple, fearless action impossible. " The ambition to be esteemed by my fellow naturalists was," as he himself said in later years, his object in life. Naturally, therefore, he was tortured by unending doubt, unending uncertainty. Remarks such as the following (written to Hooker in 1844) are common in his letters. " At last gleams of light have come, and I am almost convinced (quite contrary to the opinion I started with) that species are not (it is like confessing a murder) immutable." " Gleams of light," indeed—when years before the light had been dazzlingly bright !

Physically Darwin was remarkably healthy. When a young man he had indulged in sport with considerable success and on one occasion in the course of his travels, he and another man were alone able to fetch water for the rest of the party who were prostrated by fatigue. Even in later life long journeys tired him little. But the constant uncertainty as to whether or no he should take the final plunge—an uncertainty that he allowed to haunt him for twenty years—more than unnerved him. As a result he suffered almost continuous ill health of a vague and indefinable kind. Even mild conversation with friends who came to the house would usually upset him so much that he could not sleep properly at night. Evolution became the one all-pervading idea of his life, dominating even his private correspondence to an almost unbelievable degree. And even after twenty years Darwin, far from being nearer a final decision, was farther from it than ever. Then at last the inevitable happened. His hand was forced.

One morning in June 1858 there arrived a letter from A. R. Wallace, then at Ternate in the Moluccas, asking for advice on a MS. he was enclosing. Darwin read the MS. and was startled to find that it consisted of an epitome of the views that he himself had for so long withheld from

the world.   Only two years before, Lyell had warned him
that Wallace would be there first if he did not hurry up
and, for the sake of establishing priority, Charles had
begun to write " a *very thin* and little volume " on the subject
of natural selection.   But work had gone badly.   The idea
of a small volume had been abandoned and dreams of
portly tomes had again filled Darwin's horizon—tomes
that seemed to increase continuously in number and size
as the ink dried on the paper.   Now, at last, the dreaded
event had happened, exactly as Lyell had said it would.
Distracted and deeply upset Charles wrote to Lyell :
" Your words have come true with a vengeance that I
should be forestalled. . . .   If Wallace had my MS. sketch
written out in 1842, he could not have made a better short
abstract !   Even his terms now stand as heads of my
chapters."   Darwin was put to the test.   The honourable
thing had to be done.   The MS. would have to be sent to
a scientific journal.   Charles wrote piteous wavering letters
to Lyell and Hooker.   One day he was writing to say that
he was willing to let Wallace have all the credit, the next
that he wanted recognition for all the years of labour that
he himself had done.   What should he do ?   In the past
he had constantly protested that he had no interest in fame
and priority for it was truth and truth alone that mattered.
That sounded good in theory, but how could he simply
look on while a mere youngster stole the reputation that
should have been his ?

In the end Hooker arranged for fragments of Darwin's
earlier writings—his draft of 1842 and a letter sent to Asa
Gray the year before—to be combined with the Wallace
MS.   Before long a paper, purporting to have been written
by Wallace and Darwin jointly, was read before the Linnean
Society by the Secretary and published before the end of
1858.

Henceforth the die was cast.   Darwin could neither
withdraw nor procrastinate any longer.   His only course

lay in seeking to establish his idea, by presenting the evidence, before it could be scorched by the scientific opinion of the day. But the evidence, he decided, was so vast that it would still take years to compile. He must content himself, first of all, with a mere summary. Even this summary soon became a good sized volume but it was completed at last and sent to John Murray, the publisher. Mr. Murray found it " as absurd as though one should contemplate a fruitful union between a poker and a rabbit." But he published the book and so, towards the end of 1859, Darwin's most famous work appeared under the ambitious title, *The Origin of Species*. His larger work, of which this was but the forerunner, never saw completion.[1]

To-day, Darwin's theory of evolution is so well known that the barest summary of his views will suffice. Darwin started by assuming that the young always differ in innumerable small ways from their parents. He supposed that these differences were heritable and that they occurred at random in all conceivable directions. He argued, accordingly, that the trivial differences that enable the new generation to live longer, to mate sooner, or otherwise to produce more offspring, will naturally be " selected." That is to say, animals endowed with these small favourable variations will increase in numbers, while others will tend to die out. A law of nature, in fact, selects those individuals that are best fitted to survive and allows the rest to perish. The natural law functions, therefore, in a similar manner to a keeper of pigeons who produces new varieties by selecting those with the small variations that best please him.

The law of natural selection, as we shall shortly see, captivated the minds of Darwin's contemporaries. In point of fact, of course, it was neither new nor particularly

---

[1] However, as Henshaw Ward points out, it is possible to regard nearly all Darwin's biological works—on barnacles, on pangenesis, on the descent of man, on variations under domestication, on earthworms, on the fertilization of orchids, etc.—as together constituting a single commentary on his evolutionary views.

wonderful. To say that those best fitted to survive were those that did survive was, although for a long time no one noticed the fact, a mere truism. For survivors could only be identified as the best fitted to survive by the fact that they survived—an idea which brings to mind the lines of Lessing :

> "*One thing I've often thought is queer,*
> *Said Jack to Ted, the which is*
> *That wealthy folk upon our sphere*
> *Alone possess the riches.*"
> "(*Es ist doch sonderbar bestellt,*
> *Sprach Hänschen Schlau zu Vetter Fritzen,*
> *Dass nur die Reichen in der Welt*
> *Das meiste Geld besitzen*)."

In the same way Darwin was gravely pointing out that living creatures alone possessed the fitness to live.

The idea that natural selection could achieve progress had greater claim to novelty, though, as we have seen it was by no means new. Yet a third feature of Darwin's theory was his insistence on the element of struggle. Adapting the law of Malthus, he saw in nature an unending struggle for existence—a struggle so intense that only a few of each generation ever reach maturity. Darwin pointed out that in many species—especially among fishes—the number of progeny from a single female might amount to millions, of which all save a very few die soon after birth. Any slight variations that enable the young to avoid their enemies, or to obtain more food than their fellows, would increase their chance of survival, a process that would be repeated from generation to generation. Thus, as time goes on, species would become constantly better adapted for life. If the surroundings changed as a result of a migration or a physical change on the earth's surface, species would, in time, be able to adapt themselves to the new conditions.

In saying that variations might be produced by *chance*, Darwin made quite clear that the word was used only as a cloak for ignorance and that he did not wish to imply that *no* cause was at work. Thus we say that chance determines whether a coin will come down " heads " or " tails " but everybody knows that the result really depends upon the exact way in which we throw the coin. In his earlier days Charles thought that chance and natural selection would explain everything but, later on, he was increasingly disposed to allow that Lamarck's use-inheritance might have occurred now and then, though he still thought it was probably a minor factor in evolution.

After explaining his theory, Darwin proceeded to give an outline of his main grounds for believing in evolution or, as he called it, " modification by descent." There was the evidence afforded by embryology, by the fossils, by comparative anatomy, by the presence of vestigial organs and by the geographical distribution of animals— especially on the islands he had visited. He concluded that the evidence for evolution was overwhelming, and he closed the book with the well-known words : " It may be asked how far I extend the doctrine of the modification of species. . . . I cannot doubt that the theory of descent with modification embraces all the members of the same great class or kingdom. I believe that animals are descended from at most only four or five progenitors, and plants from an equal or lesser number. Analogy would lead me one step further, namely, to the belief that all animals and plants are descended from some one prototype. But analogy may be a deceitful guide. Nevertheless," he continued, " all living things have much in common. . . . Therefore I should infer from analogy that probably all the organic beings which have ever lived upon this earth have descended from one primordial form into which life was first breathed by the Creator."

The immediate effects of Darwin's book were surprisingly meagre. It attracted a good deal less attention than the *Vestiges* had done and for years was totally ignored by some of the best journals of the day.

The Times contained a laudatory review which had, however, been written in the main by Huxley. The *Athenæum* urged that the whole book consisted of endless repetition to the effect that Mr. Darwin *must* be right and that " if only we knew more the difficulties would vanish." The writer was especially critical of Darwin's shifts in the matter of palæontology.

The *Saturday Review* argued that Darwin's views, which were by no means new, were not in the least " hostile to the truths of Revelation." Mr. Darwin had clearly taken commendable care in his presentation of the case but it was not entirely convincing—especially as regards geology. " Discussing the subject with men of the most varied opinions," says the writer, " we have found them nearly unanimous upon one point—that there must be somewhere discoverable a true criterion of species, and that, although the *modus operandi* of Creative Power might remain concealed, the general plan of Creation would, sooner or later, be made known to us." Yet natural selection, says the writer, has come to stay. It can certainly modify species, " but we are convinced that the modifying power rests within defined limits, though these may not be discoverable by man." The *Guardian* agreed that Darwin's book must be taken seriously and that it undoubtedly proved that the number of distinct species was much smaller than had previously been supposed ; yet, the writer thought that few would wish to go as far as Darwin had gone in the matter. The *Daily News*, on the other hand, told Mr. Darwin quite plainly that he had stolen his thunder from his " master " the author of the *Vestiges*.

As for the Roman Catholics, Canon Morris told the readers of the *Dublin Review* about a Cambridge student who, shortly before his examination, was reading *Punch* instead of working at his sums which lay unfinished on the table. To a friend who expressed great surprise at such conduct he replied, " Ah ! You don't understand. While I'm sitting here, they are cancelling one another out on the table!" In the same way, thought the Canon, good Catholics could afford to watch the scientific theories cancel one another out. Not long ago, it had been said that the races of mankind differed so greatly that they could not all have been derived from Adam and Eve. Now came Mr. Darwin proclaiming, not merely that all *men* had the same ancestor, but that so too, perhaps, had all living organisms! Clearly, there was no need to be unduly concerned!

Thus, in a desultory and sporadic way, the controversy continued. It was soon clear that Darwin's book would receive much less attention that the *Vestiges* and that the public generally were not disposed to re-open a question which had been closed little more than a decade before.

The scientific world, also, was almost wholly against the *Origin*. In later years T. H. Huxley, speaking of the year 1860, described the situation by saying: "The supporters of Mr. Darwin's views were numerically extremely insignificant. There is not the slightest doubt that if a general council of the Church scientific had been held at that time, we should have been condemned by an overwhelming majority."

In part, personal matters seem also to have come into the story. Darwin had had no university training in biology and, having retired to live on a private income in the country, he held no responsible position in science. Naturally enough, those scientists who were dependent upon the meagre incomes available to scientific men in those days, hardly looked upon him as one of themselves. Nor would all of them have been willing to give the credit for a fundamental scientific discovery to an outsider—no matter how well it was deserved.

The situation was also complicated by the attitude of Richard Owen. At that time Owen was the greatest living anatomist, a man with unrivalled knowledge and experience in research. But success in science had gone to his head. He produced an unending series of scientific papers which he read at learned societies and he always saw to it that they were reported at inordinate length. He was self-opinionated to an extreme and reluctant to admit that one new discovery within his province had been made by anyone else. Often he would quote his own earlier writings to prove that he had anticipated everything worth anticipating. In manner, he was possessed of what has been described as a frighteningly bland oily politeness, while Emerson speaks of his " surgical smile."

At the time of the publication of the *Origin*, Owen was engaged in a petty feud with Thomas Huxley, his former pupil. Their controversy was largely concerned with the brains of apes and men—Owen stressing the differences and Huxley the resemblances. *Punch* (in 1861) later referred to their difference of opinion in the well-known lines :

> " *Am I satyr or man ?*
> *Pray tell me, who can,*
> *And settle my place in the scale ,*
> *A man in ape's shape,*
> *An anthropoid ape*
> *Or a monkey deprived of a tail ?* "

Hearing that Huxley was disposed to approve of Darwin's views, Owen wrote a vigorous and spiteful attack on the *Origin* in the *Edinburgh Review*, and thus threw against it the weight of his anatomical and palæontological knowledge. Darwin considered the attack spiteful to a degree, yet its most devastating criticism was merely that Darwin's book left " the determination of the origin of species very nearly where the author found it." Owen pointed out that since variations are not normally transmitted at all, it was difficult to see how Darwin's suggested theory could hold water. As for the assertion of Charles that previous writers were " one and all firmly convinced that each of the well-marked forms or species was at the first independent- ally created," Owen well remarked that he had read all the books to which Darwin referred, but, to quote his own words : " our experience has been that the monographers referred to have rarely committed themselves to any conjectural hypothesis whatever, upon the origin of the species which they have closely studied." Darwin was, in fact, knocking down an Aunt Sally. It is of interest to note that, in all this, Owen had not the slightest interest in supporting what he disdainfully called, " literal scripturalism."[1]

In other directions also the *Origin* fared no better—it was, for example, vigorously opposed by Sedgwick at Cambridge. Lyell, too, who had been personally helpful to Darwin, was opposed, though he changed his opinion five years later.

At the end of June, 1860 the British Association was to meet at Oxford and it seemed that there, also, Darwin's views would meet with no better reception. Darwin had intended to go but his usual ailments made him change his mind. Owen, too, though he went to some of the meetings, never joined in the battle concerning the *Origin*.

Darwin was by no means in the limelight. Indeed, his name was not so much as mentioned by Lord Wrottesley in his review of the scientific advances of the previous year. Nevertheless, the promoters of the meeting decided that it would be well if Darwin's book were briefly alluded to in one paper. They decided that the versatile Dr. Charles Daubeny, the Professor of Botany at Oxford, who had previously been Professor of Chemistry, and was also a renowned Geologist, might be asked to mention the matter. So on Thursday, June 28, Daubeny delivered a learned and rather dull lecture on *The Final Causes of Plants*. Towards the end of the lecture he devoted a few minutes to Darwin's ideas. His line of reasoning is most interesting. At that time a number of chemists were drawing attention to the fact that certain chemical elements

[1] Neither, for that matter, had Agassiz, Darwin's greatest opponent in America. Agassiz was not a religious man and never went to church. (See H. Ward, *Charles Darwin*, 1927, p. 279).

bore close resemblances to one another. Indeed, it was possible to classify many of the elements into groups according to their properties. It was, therefore, gradually becoming clear that the elements were not all distinct and unalterable kinds of matter as had hitherto been supposed, but that those within the same groups were connected in ways not yet understood. It seemed likely, indeed, that if only we knew how, elements within the same group might be derivable from one another. But it was unreasonable to carry the argument too far. In some instances elements differed so greatly in their properties, that no responsible chemist would go so far as to suggest that inter-conversion would ever be possible.

In biology, the situation was closely similar. Some species were so much alike that they fell into natural groups and, within these groups, it seemed reasonable to suppose that species were not eternally fixed. Mr. Darwin had put forward a possible and very reasonable theory to explain how changes might have taken place. Yet, as with the elements, so with biological organisms, the philosophically-minded scientist would not jump to the conclusion that *all* organisms were connected. Sharp and unbridgeable chasms between the different fundamental structures no doubt existed, even though our ignorance was such that they could not be delineated. In closing, the lecturer said that he would accept Darwin's theory up to a point. But " he wished not to be considered as advocating it to the extent to which the author seemed disposed to carry it." He would accept transformism, but not transformism unlimited. More research was, he said, clearly needed " to fix the limits within which the doctrine proposed by Mr. Darwin may assist us in distinguishing varieties from species."

Since Huxley was known to favour Darwin he was invited to comment on the paper. The balanced view given by Daubeny being quite out of his line, he had nothing to say. Owen rose at once and delivered himself of a completely irrelevant harangue on the differences between the brains of men and apes. Young Huxley then roundly declared that Owen was talking nonsense and offered to prove that even his facts were wrong.

Bitter feelings had been aroused and rumour had it that Owen was planning his counter-attack. On the following Saturday it was understood that Samuel Wilberforce[1], the Bishop of Oxford, colloquially known as "Soapy Sam," would speak in a discussion on evolution. The audience that turned up was so large that it was necessary to move from the usual lecture room to the library, which, in turn, was filled to standing. Owen was to have taken the chair, but as he failed to arrive Professor Henslow took his place. Professor Draper was then called upon to read his long and dull paper on *The Intellectual Development of Europe Considered with Reference to the Views of Mr. Darwin and Others.* For an hour or more he droned on and on while the audience listened, or pretended to listen, impatiently. The meeting was then opened for discussion. The first two who attempted to speak were shouted down. A third commenced by drawing two crosses on the blackboard and asking the audience to imagine that one was a man and the other a monkey. His unusual pronunciation of the latter word was greeted with hilarious delight by the undergraduates present, who jubilantly yelled, "Mawnkey! Mawnkey!"

Then, as if realizing that the audience was waiting for him to speak, up jumped "Soapy Sam," who had entered the meeting late and had pushed his way through the crowd fairly bristling with importance. He proceeded at once to deliver himself of an oration against the new evolutionary hypothesis. It was obvious to many in the audience that the substance of his lecture was not first-hand—that he had probably been primed by Sedgwick, or perhaps it might have been Owen. At first the Bishop was jovial, suave and affable. He spoke with polished

[1] Samuel Wilberforce, third son of William Wilberforce, was a prominent High Churchman and had been Bishop of Oxford since 1845.

English, making sly but kindly digs at Charles, and Huxley too. His arguments largely verged on the ludicrous. According to Mr. Darwin, so he said, all life was derived from "some primitive fungus." When once Charles had succeeded in proving this, said the Bishop, "we shall dismiss our pride and avow, with the characteristic humility of philosophy, our unsuspected cousinship with the mush-rooms." Or again—"Is it credible," he asked, looking around the audience with his happy smile, "is it credible that all favourable varieties of turnips are tending to become men?"[1] Such rubbish, and much more besides, was delivered in so persuasive a manner that the chairman had no heart to stop him. As the Bishop warmed to his task, the sly personal references became more pronounced, and when, after half an hour's brilliant rhetoric, he deemed it wise to finish, he looked straight at Huxley with a sardonic smile and demanded to be told whether it was through his grandfather or his grand-mother that Huxley owed his monkey ancestry.

The Bishop's oration was greeted with howls of delight, for the evolutionists in the assembly were a mere handful. In a few moments the audience from all sides was calling upon Huxley to reply. He remained, however, firmly seated until Henslow, from the chair, asked him if he had anything to say.

At this invitation Huxley rose. There was some applause but it came only from one small quarter of the hall, where his friends were sitting closely grouped together. Huxley began by saying that he had risen only in the interests of science. The Bishop's comments, he said, had not altered his opinion about Mr. Darwin's theory, which was the best explanation of the formation of species that had yet been put forward. He then mentioned a number of scientific points and made it clear by implication that he hardly thought the Bishop was competent to deal with a

[1] The Bishop's speech was not reported but is said to have followed closely on the lines of his attack in the *Quarterly Review*, from which these quotations are taken.

subject about which he knew so little. To the argument that it was inconceivable that a man could be descended from a lower animal, he replied by pointing his pencil towards the Bishop, and remarking that his lordship was at one time an embryo smaller than the pencil's end. If evolution from an embryo was possible, why not evolution from a lower animal ? At last he closed with his famous parting thrust. He would not, he said, be at all ashamed of having an ape for an ancestor, but would be very much ashamed if he knew that he had been descended from one " who, not content with equivocal success in his own sphere of activity, plunges into scientific questions with which he has no real acquaintance, only to obscure them by an aimless rhetoric, and distract the attention of the hearers from the real point at issue by eloquent digressions and skilled appeals to religious prejudice."

The audience was electrified, for in those days great respect was paid to bishops. A woman fainted and was carried out. But while he had been speaking Huxley had slowly won his audience over. As he made his thrusts, applause grew in volume until, at the end, his former enemies cheered him wildly.

The discussion continued. Among those who spoke was Admiral FitzRoy, under whom Darwin had served on the *Beagle*. The meeting was wound up by a speech from Hooker, who again attacked the Bishop both for his ignorance and for his interference in scientific matters. To the Bishop's claim that " the theory was so absurd that no scientific man could for a moment think that it was in any degree worth considering," Hooker replied by saying that as he, a scientist, thought the theory worth considering, it was up to the Bishop to apologize for addressing the meeting in such a manner. The Bishop, by now thoroughly subdued, made no defence, but Huxley has left us the record : " In justice to the Bishop, I am bound to say that he bore no malice."

The British Association of 1860 formed the topic of conversation for many a day. Steadily but surely scientific opinion began to change and the supporters of Darwin and Huxley, at first an insignificant minority, became a majority in less than a decade.

As for Charles Darwin, he stayed at home. His heart palpitated as he summoned up enough courage to read the reviews of his book. His headaches lasted for days on end. Some of the reviews almost convinced him that he had made a ghastly mistake. It seemed that he had made a fool of himself after all. At the time of the Oxford meetings he had an " almost continuous headache for forty-eight hours " and, spent his time " thinking what a useless burthen I was to myself and all others." Then letters from Hooker and Huxley arrived and he began once more to feel like a naughty schoolboy—though not quite naughty enough to attack a " live Bishop " all by himself. Still, there was just a chance of success, for his two friends suffered from none of his own inhibitions. Perhaps, then, pressure gang tactics might do what argument had already failed to do. Hurriedly he wrote to Huxley : " If we can once make a compact set of believers we shall in time conquer. . . . Yours very tired, C. D."

The plan succeeded. Within a year the scientific world had been divided into pro-Darwinians and anti-Darwinians —each side largely unwilling to consider the merits of their opponents' case or to reach a balanced judgment on the matter. And the pressure gang tactics were so successful that as time passed the Darwinians increased steadily in number and influence while their opponents became fewer and fewer.

As for the bishops—it is said that they soon began to spend sleepless nights whenever an extra ape-like man or an extra man-like ape was unearthed. And a bishop's wife, on hearing of the new theory of man's origin, said : " Let's hope it isn't true and if it is, that it will not become generally known."

CHAPTER V

WHAT DARWIN ACCOMPLISHED

THE "ORIGIN OF SPECIES," SAYS ONE WRITER, WAS A veritable Magna Charta of intellectual liberties, accomplishing more in this direction than any other document in the whole history of mankind. Darwin did more for the liberation of human thought, says another writer, than the combined careers of Alexander the Great, Julius Cæsar, Napoleon and all the other so-called liberators of history. He re-orientated the thinking of an entire world and the gratitude we owe him can scarcely be measured.

What was the secret of Darwin's success? In what way did he emancipate human thought? Why were so many grateful to him? These are some of the questions which we shall seek to answer in the present chapter.

First of all, then, what was the secret of Darwin's success? How was it that, although evolutionary views had been put forward repeatedly before Darwin's day and had hitherto met only with merciless criticism—yet—after the ill-fated meeting of the British Association in 1860, the doctrine of evolution made such remarkable progress that scientific opinion throughout the world changed within the course of a decade?

The factors operating for success were many. First and foremost, of course, was the fact that Darwin's views were not unfounded, but were ably supported with a mass of new and fascinating evidence. The story he unfolded could hardly have been presented in a more plausible form. Yet this by itself would not have convinced the scientific world. Success was equally due to the fact that the times were ripe—and ripe in more senses than one.

In the earlier half of the nineteenth century the

transformist doctrines were almost wholly abandoned in
favour of the fixity of species. Cuvier, in France, had misused
his influence to prevent believers in the mutability of species
from being appointed to important posts. As time drew
on, the doctrine of the fixity of species was carried to ever
more ridiculous lengths. Agassiz, in America, claimed
that even man consisted of eight races, each separately
created, while others improved on this estimate by raising
the number of special creations to more than sixty. Transformism was also denied to the innumerable varieties of
insects—the number of special creations necessary reaching
fantastic limits. The scientific stage was clearly set for
reaction, a reaction greatly helped by Lyell's insistence on
uniformitarianism in geology, which prepared the ground
for uniformitarianism in biology.

Another factor at work was the astonishing prejudice
shown by Wilberforce at the British Association, which
caused many to imagine that disbelief in evolution must
somehow be connected with theological prejudice. All
those, again, who secretly resented the way in which
prominent clergy sought to invade meetings of a scientific
character, obscuring facts by oratory, were doubtless disposed to join the Darwinian clique. Evolution afforded
an excellent stick with which to beat the theologian.

Sociological factors were also at work. So far as the
public was concerned, not only had the way been prepared
by the *Vestiges* and similar writings, but the idea of evolution by natural selection of the fittest was a view that
appealed particularly to industrialists and the upper classes,
who saw in the doctrine a universal law of nature that
would serve to justify their own grasping practices.
Evolution, also, was welcome to the politician, forming,
as it did, an excellent rationalization for war. Added to
this, England was in her hey-day of her glory. Trade was
expanding, the standard of living was rising, social ser-
vices were being increased and budget surpluses were the

order of the day. Such conditions favoured optimism and, as Bertrand Russell has pointed out, they therefore favoured the spread of evolution which offered a philosophy of optimism.

There were other factors, too, of a more subtle but no less interesting nature. As we have already had occasion to note, the middle of the nineteenth century saw a series of brilliant discoveries in physical science. Organic chemistry opened up a way of determining exact arrangements among atoms. Physicists were elaborating the molecular theory of gases with astonishing success, were unifying electricity and magnetism and laying the foundations of thermodynamics. Astronomers were discovering the extra-galactic nebulæ and were learning how to classify the stars by their spectra. Every field of research was beginning to hum with activity.

Such were the advances of physical science. But what had biology to show for itself? Nothing at all. Only an increasing mass of data about natural history, all totally undigested. Indeed, writers of the time were fully aware of the situation. Buckle, in his *History of Civilization* (1861) complained bitterly of the way in which scientific facts (especially in biology) had accumulated for two centuries until they had reached a total far greater than any memory could retain. "In vain do we demand that they should be generalized and reduced to order. Instead of that, the heap continues to swell. We want ideas and we get more facts. . . . We are in possession of a huge and incoherent mass of observations which . . . unless they are connected by some presiding idea, will be utterly useless."

Darwin supplied the key that was missing. Even if his key did not altogether fit the door—even if it sometimes seemed as if he was using ignorance rather than knowledge to support his views—it was so much better to have a theory of some kind than to be without one at all, that

his contemporaries were ultimately willing to accept his
views.   A hungry man is not too particular as to the kind
of food he eats.

But there was more to it than this.   The news of the
great discoveries in physical science had begun to permeate
society.   They produced a feeling of exhilaration and
excitement among those who were able to understand
what was " going on," and an opposite feeling of frustration and inferiority among the rest who could not even
begin to grasp what they were all about.   Darwin himself
suffered in this way.   To friends he would write in terms
of almost pathetic humility about the new physical discoveries reported at the British Association.   He was
always deeply sorry that he had found mathematics " repug-
nant " when he was young and would speak of those who
understood even a modicum of this subject as endowed
with " an extra sense."

A feeling of humiliation and frustration is rarely permanent.   Sooner or later the personality must rise above it ;
but this is often achieved in the worst possible way—that
of hatred and resentment.   Unfortunately, such resentment became a major factor in nineteenth century science
—nor has it yet disappeared.   The physical scientist,
accustomed to disciplined quantitative thinking, despised
the new upstart " science " that sought to solve every
problem by words and the repeated use of such catch-
phrases as " if we may grant."   The non-exact scientists,
on the other hand, when once they had begun to spin
their theories, refused any longer to stand in awe of physical
science.   Instead, they came to detest the self-conceit of
those who imagined that no science was worthy of the
name unless it employed mathematical equations and
graphical representations.

Darwin's attitude was typical of his day.   When the *Origin*
was published, he was cut to the quick by a review written
by Samuel Haughton.   "It is evidently by Haughton,

the geologist, chemist and mathematician," he writes. " It shows immeasurable conceit and contempt of all who are not mathematicians. . . . The article is a curiosity of unfairness and arrogance." Of another mathematician, he writes, " W. Hopkins . . . like Haughton, despises the reasoning power of all naturalists." Lyell, the geologist, supported Darwin and was accustomed to express the utmost contempt of mathematical reasoning.

By now, perhaps, the point will be clear. Psychologically, the law of evolution by natural selection afforded a means by which Darwin and his non-mathematical contemporaries could transform their feelings of inferiority into grounds of superiority. It enabled them to hope that henceforth real scientific advance would be achieved without a grounding in physical and mathematical thought.

Darwin, in short, had discovered a highly ingenious way by means of which not only biologists but the ordinary intelligent reading public of his day could " catch up " with modern science. Henceforth they could read of enormous strides made in physical science with equanimity. True, these advances remained unintelligible, but it was impossible for any one individual to know all about every advance that was taking place in every sphere of knowledge. Enough if he could understand and grasp the significance of one such advance—the theory of natural selection—which, so he was told *ad nauseam*, was one of the most, perhaps *the* most, wonderful discovery of the day. And this he could do without calculus, without a grounding in physics and chemistry, without the need for years of work to be spent in a laboratory. Any moderately intelligent reader—provided he made some effort—could master Darwin's *Origin* and so could share the thoughts of one who was proclaimed to be as wise as Galileo or Newton, Faraday or Clerk Maxwell.

From the earliest days, evolution naturally appealed chiefly to those with an anti-mathematical bias, Darwin among them.   There were exceptions, of course, but on the whole the great leaders of physical science in the nineteenth century—Clerk Maxwell, Faraday, Kelvin and others—regarded it with scepticism.   And from that day to this, the most dogmatic evolutionists have very often been anti-mathematical in their outlook.   H. G. Wells, for instance, tells us that when he was a student he was completely unable to appreciate physical arguments, even in their most elementary forms.   Again, we read of E. B. Poulton that : " He first read the *Origin of Species* in 1875 as an undergraduate and throughout his life it was almost like a Bible to him. . . . Mathematics was as incomprehensible to him as to the master (Moseley at Oxford) he served."[1]

One outstanding achievement of Darwin lay in the fact that he broke the spell of physical science.   Henceforth " science " became the monopoly of all who chose to apply the word to their own studies.   Marx, deeply stirred by Darwin's writings, could appeal to the working classes to rebel in the name of a " science " of history.   Capitalists and politicians could claim that " science " was on their side.   Henceforth vague and unsupported conjectures about the development of language, of race, of cultures, of religion, or of social customs, could all be called " scientific."   Darwin showed how the journalist, the popular writer, the political propagandist—all, in fact, who resented exact or disciplined thought because they could not be bothered to master it, could have their revenge for the inferiority of feelings that it had occasioned them. Nor were the pseudo-scientists slow to follow Darwin's lead.

This violent revolt from exact science is illustrated best of all, perhaps, in the writings of Herbert Spencer, who poured forth volume after volume of the wildest speculations in an attempt to provide a " scientific " philosophy

[1] *Nature,* 1944, **153,** 15.

of life. Needless to say, the exact scientists of the day were astounded and revolted by his activities. In 1874, for instance, when he was invited to speak at the British Association, he caused widespread dismay by a speech in which, as we read, he regretted that so many members of the British Association " were in the habit of employing the word *force* in a sense too limited and definite to be of any use in a complete theory of evolution. He had himself always been careful to preserve that largeness of meaning which was too often lost sight of in elementary works. This was best done by using the word sometimes in one sense and sometimes in another, and in this way he trusted that he had made the word occupy a sufficiently large field of thought."

It was likely enough that Charles Darwin was scarcely conscious of the way in which he was saving the day for the non-mathematicians. But if his motives in this respect were unconscious, and in no way blameworthy, it is difficult to exonerate him so completely in other directions.

To Darwin's contemporaries, it was an humiliating thought that man, so noble and wise, should have sprung from an ape. When Galileo proved that the earth was not, after all, at the centre of the universe, the result had been hardly more shattering to human vanity. But science had now humiliated man still further. Darwin had discovered —or thought he had discovered—that *homo sapiens* had not even been created by the God of the Universe, but was the mere descendant of an idiotic chattering animal.

Such was the disconcerting " discovery." Men were only prepared to accept its truth because, in other ways, the theory of evolution itself pandered to their vanity. It saved them from the humiliation that science had brought in its train ; it provided the more sceptical with a new positive philosophy with which they might counter the dogmas of the theologians ; above all, it enabled them to look upon " sin " from the objective evolutionary viewpoint which saw in a sinful act not something wicked and blameworthy, but a relic of the beast which had not yet been thrown off in man's triumphant evolutionary progress towards the stars. These advantages could not lightly be thrown away. Nevertheless, it was still a little shattering to learn of so humble an ancestry. Men were unlikely to remain satisfied for long unless the new humiliation could in turn be made a ground of pride.

In this matter Darwin himself obligingly led the way and here we see him at his worst. He expressed sentiments that have strongly appealed to his followers, even up to our own day, sentiments directly encouraging human pride. " Man," he said, " may be excused for feeling some pride at having risen, though not through his own exertions, to the very summit of the organic scale ; and the fact of his having thus risen, may give him hopes for a still higher destiny in the distant future."[1]

It hardly needs to be pointed out that such teaching is neither sensible nor even consistent. How anyone can rightly feel pride in events which happened hundreds of thousands or even millions of years before he was born, neither Darwin nor his followers have ever bothered to explain. We do not feel *proud* of the fact (if it is a fact) that the earth once left the sun, or of the fact that the ancient land-bridge between England and the continent is now covered with water, thus making our country an island. For such things we may, indeed, be thankful, but not proud. And as for bright hopes of the future it is, perhaps, enough to quote the Biblical proverb : " Let not him that girdeth on his harness boast himself as he that taketh it off."

So deeply did this teaching of Darwin become entrenched that even to-day, after the lapse of sixty or seventy years since the hey-day of Darwinism, many modern writers still seem incapable of divorcing evolution from self-flattery.

[1] *Descent of Man*, II, p. 405

Thus it has become almost commonplace to say, with Needham, that " human thought will never again be as it was before the facts of evolution became known to us," for " the world about him (Man) is real " (was it unreal before Darwin ?) and man, " eventually, like a child growing up . . . became conscious (!) of his ancestry. The value of his highest ideals and actions is indeed independent of their origin, but only in the light of their origin could they attain their highest dignity (how ?) and be vested with an evolutionary authority (how can evolution give them *authority*?) securer than any supernaturalism, the measure of his greatness now and the guarantee (why ? Will evolution stop race-suicide by atomic warfare ?) of untold greatness to come."[1] Or, again, Julian Huxley, after saying that science gives us a truer picture of our nature and place in the universe than any other philosophic approach, remarks that we may be " proud " of the fact that we are the dominant species.[2]

The case is even worse than might appear on the surface, for, in attempting to meet the " difficulty " that it is very humiliating to imagine oneself as having descended from an ape, both Darwin[3] and his followers[4] repeatedly urged that as we were all at one time embryos and then babies, and yet are unashamed of the fact, there is no need to be ashamed of our animal ancestry. This argument soon became, indeed, part of the stock-in-trade of Darwinian propagandists. Yet, clearly, it cuts both ways. For, if it be legitimate to compare our baby origin with our animal origin, then we ought to be as proud of having risen from the one as from the other. But the world did not need a Darwin to tell them that men and women once

[1] J. Needham, *History is on our Side*, 1946, p. 145.
[2] J. S. Huxley, *On Living in a Revolution*, 1944, p. 58, Clive Bell, *Civilization*, Pelican ed., 1938, p. 36, and Sir A. Keith, *Essays on Human Evolution*, 1946, p. 27, endorse Darwin's view that man should be proud because he has risen.
[3] *Descent*, II, p. 394, etc.
[4] See later, p. 158.

were babies—they knew it long before Darwin was born. All the grounds for pride which evolution is supposed to have bequeathed us were, therefore, present before evolution had ever been heard of.

In other ways, also, Darwin set in motion trains of thought that have left tragic consequences in their wake. Despite his teaching that man ought to feel pride on account of his having risen from the level of a beast, Darwin was, at times, only too apt to argue that man's mind was unreliable just *because* it was derived from the mind of a beast. Again and again we read that, when he thought about the universe, Darwin would " feel compelled to look to a first Cause having an intelligent mind in some degree analogous to that of man," and so he thought he ought to be called a Theist. But then his evolutionary theories would begin to intrude themselves. How " can the mind of man which has, as I fully believe, been developed from a mind as low as that possessed by the lowest animals, be trusted when it draws such grand conclusions ? " he would ask. And again, " would anyone trust in the convictions of a monkey's mind if there are any convictions in such a mind ? " As his correspondence shows, such thoughts arose in his mind whenever he was faced with theological issues, yet they never worried him in other connexions. He never doubted natural selection on the ground that, if an animal at the Zoo had become an orthodox Darwinian, no one would have taken any notice.

By such reasoning, Darwin allowed his evolutionary views to destroy all serious thinking about ultimate issues. Yet, once again he never seems to have realized for an instant that these all-pervading doubts were in no way necessarily connected with man's ancestry. We do not take the conclusions of a new-born baby or of a child very seriously, but no one thinks of arguing that philosophers are not to be trusted because they are only grown-up babies. Yet it was precisely this consideration, applied to monkeys instead of babies, that bothered Charles Darwin.

This new excuse for all-pervading doubt which Darwin suggested to his contemporaries had a considerable vogue. Indeed, it still seems to be imagined in some quarters that it forms part and parcel of evolutionary thinking. Of late years there has been a reaction to the doctrine that the proof of the pudding is not in the eating but in the cook's pedigree, and the excuse has become more disguised in character. Yet, when modern rationalist writers inform us that the human mind is unfit (not sufficiently evolved ?) to discuss transcendental problems, they are really harking back to the old difficulty which Charles Darwin raised. Like Charles they fail to observe that the same difficulty might be raised against thinking at any level.

Darwin's doubts about the competence of the human mind lead us directly to his views on the subject of religion. As we have already seen, Charles was brought up to be a Christian. Nor was his Christianity formal only, for, as a boy, he learned to bring his problems and troubles to God in prayer—as is evident from his own words : "I well remember in the early part of my school life that I often had to run very quickly to be in time, and from being a fleet runner was generally successful ; but when in doubt I prayed earnestly to God to help me, and I well remember that I attributed my success to the prayers and not to my quick running and marvelled how greatly I was aided."

When studying as a medical student at Edinburgh, Charles became convinced that his father would leave him money. " My belief," he wrote in later years, " was sufficient to check any strenuous effort to learn medicine." Yet he remained a Christian and accepted the Bible implicity. After leaving Edinburgh he seems to have begun to doubt whether all the teachings of the Church of England

were Biblical.   After some months of consideration he was
satisfied and went to Cambridge in order to become a
minister of the Gospel.

It was at Cambridge that Charles first read Paley's *Natural
Theology*, a book which filled him with delight and which he
came to know almost by heart.   It was at Cambridge also
that he won the friendship of Henslow and Sedgwick—
both deeply Christian men.   On the other hand it was at
Cambridge also that Charles got into bad company, from
which he could not or would not drag himself away, and
it was there also that he began to feel a hypocrite for seeking
ordination without an inward sense that God had called
him to the ministry.

On his voyage, Charles continued to profess Christianity.
But once again, his lack of enthusiasm is somewhat striking.
In his letters home, he scarcely ever mentioned God, and
then only in almost hackneyed expressions (" God bless
you ").[1]   For a modern young man, this would be in no
way unusual, but we must remember that in the early nineteenth century there was far less reticence than there is
to-day about religious matters.   Not only in private
letters, but even in scientific papers, writers felt no hesitation
in speaking of God in a manner that was evidently natural
and sincere.   And Darwin was no ordinary naval man but
one whose avowed object was to spend his life preaching
the Gospel as a minister of religion.   When we bear this
fact in mind his description of the work of the missionaries
at Tahiti is little short of astonishing.   " The missionaries
have done much in improving their (the Tahitians') moral
character, and still more in teaching them the arts of
civilization " he writes.   But he does not tell us whether
the natives were being brought to know and love God.
For all this, he went to a good deal of trouble in helping
forward the mission work.

[1] *Charles Darwin and the Voyage of the Beagle.*   Ed. Nora Barlow,
1945.

As already noted, on one occasion during the voyage, Darwin quoted the Gospel in defence of a certain point in morals, and was laughed at by the crew. Certainly FitzRoy, his constant companion, was a convinced Christian, so that Darwin was not without Christian companionship. Nor is there any evidence that he reacted strongly against the rather narrow fundamentalism of his friend, for a close friendship between them continued for many years to come.

On returning home, Darwin read further books about Christianity. For long he still intended to be ordained, but his notes and specimens kept him busy and he decided to finish his scientific work first of all. This task proved unending and, unconsciously at least, Darwin probably wanted it to be unending. As the years passed, doubts gradually began to assail him. First of all his faith in the Old Testament was shattered. Then he could no longer believe in the miracles of the New. Finally he was left wondering whether Christianity was a Divine revelation at all.

For a while, so he tells us, Charles would day-dream of wonderful new MSS that had been unearthed in the Middle East, which would substantiate the Gospel record and set his mind at rest. He cites this as evidence that at heart he truly wanted to believe and that his loss of faith was no fault of his own. Yet, as Warfield [1] has pointed out, his words really point to the opposite conclusion for he finishes by saying : " I found it more and more difficult, with free scope given to my imagination, to invent evidence which would convince me." No remark could reveal more clearly that, while pretending to himself that he wanted to believe, Charles was really determined at all costs *not* to believe and so, in order to rationalize his unbelief, he steadily raised the level of evidence he required before he would be convinced.

Towards 1850, these idle fancies ceased, and, at the age

[1] B. B. Warfield, *Studies in Theology*, 1932, pp. 541 ff.

of forty or a little over, Darwin ceased to regard himself as a Christian and began to describe himself as an agnostic. Henceforth, he no longer professed much interest in theology ; biology was more important. In later years his children reported that they never heard him mention religion in the home. His loss of faith, however, was so slow that it did not, so he says, cause him any acute pain at the time.

Eventually, of course, he abandoned his earlier plan of seeking ordination and, as he was now well provided for by his father, and further moneys came to him through the death of his brother and the royalties on his books, no financial anxiety was involved.

Such are the outward facts about the decline of Darwin's faith in Christianity—the facts recorded by most of his biographers. Yet there is abundant evidence that they tell only half the story. Darwin's loss of faith must have had a far greater effect upon his mind than he himself realized at the time. Kempf points out the very significant fact that the beginnings of his unbelief brought with them the first important instance of illness.[1] As Darwin's religion faded, so he consecrated his life to science with what has aptly been described as an almost religious enthusiasm. But his illnesses became worse and worse.

What was wrong with him ? Nothing, apparently. Indeed, his friends generally supposed that he was shamming, for he looked well and that his constitution was sound would appear to follow from the fact that he lived to an old age. Yet he was a chronic invalid. Unfavourable reviews of his books gave him continuous headaches ; even half an hour's discussion with a fellow naturalist about scientific matters would render him incapable of work for hours. If he met people in society, anxiety afflicted him. " My health almost always suffered from the

[1] E. J. Kempf, op. cit, p. 225.

excitement, violent shivering and vomiting being thus brought on," he wrote. His constant preoccupation became one of protecting himself from anticipations and conflicts while his chronic anxiety brought on the usual digestive and nutritional troubles.

In addition Charles Darwin was morbid and self-critical to an extreme. His letters abound with the typical language associated with a feeling of guilt. A letter " was vilely written and is now vilely expressed," his MS was a " foul copy," he was " hot with indignation " and unable to sleep, and so on.

Psychologically there can be little doubt as to the meaning of these symptoms. Charles Darwin was suffering from a feeling of guilt. But what was worrying him ? At first sight, the answer might appear to be clear. As we saw in the last chapter, he experienced considerable anxiety with regard to his theory of evolution—fearing that it might be rejected and damage his reputation. But that this was not *primarily* at the root of his trouble is clear from the fact that, even after he had won the battle for evolution, even after his reputation was assured, his psychological suffering continued as before. Fear of the outcome of the evolutionary battle, in short, was only a symptom of a deeper and more fundamental anxiety and feeling of guilt.

The answer to the riddle is not far to seek. Darwin's trouble almost certainly lay in the suppression of his religious needs. His life was one long attempt to escape from Paley, to escape from the Church, to escape from God. It is this that explains so much that would otherwise be incongruous in his life and character.

First of all, let us consider the doctrine of natural selection. Darwin went to great pains to explain that he had only discovered this truth after twenty years of painful collection of facts which he had sifted and re-sifted a thousand times. He was determined to find the truth and the truth alone : it was only a passionate desire for truth which compelled him now at last to make his theories known.

That is what Darwin wished the outer world to believe. No one to-day accepts his story. He had thought of natural selection twenty years before and had long since made up his mind on the subject. Moreover, the evidence shows that Charles was not primarily interested in the truth or otherwise of natural selection at all, but was very much interested in the possibilities of using it to avoid the force of Paley's *Natural Theology*.

At the time of the publication of the *Origin*, Lyell wrote to Darwin pointing out that even though the theory of natural selection might be true, it still would not account for all forms of life. The evidence suggested strongly that not everything could have come into existence as Darwin supposed ; it was still just as necessary as before to believe that God had intervened at times—at any rate in the evolution of man. Charles read the letter but he would have none of it. " I would give absolutely nothing for the theory of natural selection if it requires miraculous additions at any one stage of descent," he replied. Of course it would be necessary to have some sort of an original creation, just as " philosophers assume the existence of a power of attraction without any explanation." But granted that, his theory would explain everything else. Even a primitive mud fish would do as a start and natural selection would see to the rest. In the *Origin* he used words unchanged which he had penned in his 1837 notebook ; " From the war of nature, from famine and death, the most exalted object which we are capable of conceiving, namely the production of the higher animals, directly follows." God, in short, might possibly be needed at the start, but He must be kept out of the universe as much as possible, and only thought of in the vaguest possible way—as vaguely as physicists thought of Him when they wondered about the origin of gravity. With this extreme position, Darwin did not remain permanently satisfied. In later years he was forced to admit that factors other than natural selection had their place in evolution. He was even slightly more willing to see the hand of God in nature, though the God he hankered after was of the impersonal kind. Indeed, he said he would be perfectly willing to believe in God if only the idea of God could be brought into line with scientific concepts—that is to say, if only God could be depersonalized.

Natural selection, in short, was a substitute for God—or, at least, for a God who takes an active interest in the world. Deism might still be true but the God of Deism was as far removed from man as the gods of the Roman pantheon. Till Darwin's day the argument from design had reigned supreme. " Then," as Romanes put it, " with a suddenness only less surprising than its completeness the end came ; the fountains of this great deep were broken up by the power of one man and never in the history of thought has a change been effected of a comparable order of magnitude."[1]

When his over-confident moods had passed, Darwin would sink into a state of child-like innocence. He did not really want to be dogmatic. He was deeply conscious of his ignorance. Indeed, he did not really know anything about the origins of things, and certainly made no pretence of having discovered how species had come into existence. He very much regretted his misleading title, the *Origin of Species* : if only he had been more thoughtful at the time he would have chosen a different title, but now it was too late. In revising the *Origin* he felt he had gone too far in his rejection of theology and more than once he added the telling words " by the Creator " when referring to the original creation of the first forms of life. But again, he could not make up his mind. In later days, when Bastian was describing the experiments in which he claimed

[1] G. J. Romanes, *Nature*, 1881, **24**, 505.

to have manufactured innumerable varieties of living
organisms by spontaneous generation, Charles was simply
itching to believe it all. Bastian claimed to have made
living organisms out of nutrient solutions which, according
to him, contained not an atom of nitrogen. Darwin's
mind rebelled. Yet, despite all, he had the feeling that
spontaneous generation *must* be right after all. " I am
bewildered and astonished by his statements," he wrote
to Wallace, " but am not convinced, though on the whole,
it seems to me probable that Archaeobiosis is true." He
hoped he would " live to see " it " proved true."

For year after year, Darwin carried on a discussion with
various friends on the subject of design in nature. Throughout he showed the same vacillation. One moment he
thought he could do without design ; the next, his reason
told him that the evidence for design by a personal God
was overwhelming. He was for ever seeking an escape
from theology but never able to find it.

In 1862 J. D. Hooker, the botanist, challenged Darwin's
claim that natural selection was in any sense a creative
agency. Hooker's letter is lost, but from Darwin's replies
it is clear that he said something like this : " Your theory
of evolution by natural selection implies that if every organism had survived and produced offspring, then every kind
of plant and animal that exists and has ever existed would
have been produced without any natural selection at all
(as well, of course, as myriads of others). In other words
all the characters present in all organisms were the necessary consequences of the earliest and most primitive
organism."[1]

Darwin had never thought of this before. For a few
anxious days, he realized that Paley could not be disposed
of as easily as he had imagined. He " was fairly pitched
head over heels with astonishment." Yet to Hooker's
claim that " every single difference which we see might

[1] See J. R. Baker, *Hibbert Journal*, 1946, **45**, 31.

have occurred without any selection," he could only go on to say : " I do and have always fully agreed."

Thus, accepting Hooker's argument, Darwin was forced towards the view that the earliest organisms, though apparently so small and simple, were really so gigantically complex that they contained the potentiality of producing all the other organisms that would ever exist on earth. It followed, therefore, that if true the theory of evolution would not abolish Paley's argument from design, but would reinforce it a hundredfold. No wonder Darwin was disturbed. He had sought to escape from God : now he found his old Enemy waiting for him in a new hiding place. His confusion can scarcely be exaggerated. In letter after letter he made the lamest excuses for his inability to think clearly. Intellectually, he said, he was in " thick mud." Eventually he tried to avoid the dilemma with a laugh. If *everything* was designed, then the shape of his nose must have been designed also (Darwin felt rather sore about the shape of his nose.) So he challenged all and sundry to say whether his nasal profile was designed by the Almighty. And *if* the world was designed, then it followed that God had preordained that a particular bird should swallow a particular gnat at a particular moment in a particular place. All of which was too much for Mr. Darwin to believe. So clearly the world was not designed.

Perhaps there was never a better instance of a man throwing away the baby with the bath water. Darwin was determined to escape from design and a personal God at all costs. He did so by deciding that either *every* trivial detail in nature must be designed *or else* that there was no design at all. Since the former possibility did not ring true, he refused to discuss the subject seriously any more. As Raven has so well remarked, " His letters exhibit a resolution not to follow his thoughts to their logical conclusion."[1]

[1] C. E. Raven, *Science, Religion and the Future*, 1943.

The mental strain in which Darwin lived must have been greatly increased by another circumstance. When reviews of the *Origin* began to appear, Darwin at first found the criticisms more convincing than his own book. For a while it seemed that his attempt to escape from God had completely misfired and that his scientific reputation would suffer irremediable damage. He became ill and suffered from sleeplessness and headaches—headaches which made it impossible for him to go to the British Association in 1860. It was then that letters from Huxley and Hooker cheered him. He was not alone. Others were fighting on his side. Necessity makes strange bedfellows. There seemed to be no alternative. Darwin, until recently a Christian, would have to join forces with Thomas Henry Huxley, the inveterate hater of religion, the man who could describe Christianity as a " varying compound of some of the best and some of the worst elements of paganism and Judaism."

Unlike Darwin, Huxley had had a hard life—at school, as a student in the East End of London and later in H.M.S. *Rattlesnake* from 1847 to 1850. On coming home he decided to spend his life doing scientific research, though, in fact, he seems to have been endowed with little ability in this direction.[1] He was disgusted to find that there were scarcely four or five posts in all London which a Zoologist or Comparative Anatomist might hold. Owen, with a European reputation second only to Cuvier, had a Professorship worth less than the salary of many a bank clerk. The relatively ignorant clergy, on the other hand, could command handsome salaries for the asking. Huxley became embittered. When in his earlier years, Lord Ernle asked him why it was that he always mixed vinegar and mustard with questions that to many people were

---

[1] H. F. Osborn (*Impressions of Great Naturalists*, 1924, p. 91) remarks that although Huxley wrote on natural selection for thirty years " he never contributed a single original or novel idea to it."

matters of life and death, he replied : " My dear young man, you are not old enough to remember when men like Lyell and Murchison were not considered fit to lick the dust off the boots of a curate." Then, allowing his mind to dwell on the clergy, he continued : " I should like to get my heel into their mouths and scr-r-unch it round."[1]

Huxley did not, at first, take very kindly to the evolution theory. In days gone by he had written a slashing review against the *Vestiges* and Darwin's *Origin* was along the same lines. But when he saw that evolution would afford him an excellent means with which to vent his spite on the clergy, he accepted it, though only guardedly at first (" subject to the production of proof that physiological species may be produced by selective breeding "—a proof that he never considered to have been forthcoming, even to the end of his days).

Huxley was also attracted towards evolutionary views for another reason. Early in his career he had been disgusted by what he had seen behind the scenes in the academic world. " You have no notion of the intrigues that go on in this blessed world of science," he had written to his sister in 1852. More than once he had resorted to stratagem in order to prevent his papers falling into the hands of Owen, who would have done his utmost to stop their publication. Huxley found his path to fame frustrated at every turn. It was becoming clearer and clearer that his ambitions would never be realized if he were to " toe the line." To sponsor some new cause and fight a battle till he won the day—there lay his chance. There were great possibilities in the line that Darwin was taking. He wrote to Darwin in flattering terms—so flattering that Charles would not show the letter to Hooker (" I had a letter from Huxley with such tremendous praise of my book that modesty prevents me sending it to you "). He offered to become his henchman. " You must recollect

[1] *Victorian Memoirs*, 1923, **239**, 215.

that some of your friends are endowed with an amount of combativeness which may stand you in good stead. I am sharpening up my claws and beak in readiness." Those words were written in December, 1859. From then on he sponsored Darwin's cause with redoubled energy—he became " Darwin's bulldog," for ever biting and barking at theologians and scientists too, until the latter accepted the Darwinian scheme of things. And it was not long before he discovered that loyalty to Darwin paid him well. He was scarcely known in the scientific world until the British Association meeting in 1860, which at once brought his name to the fore.

Charles, who might so easily have become a clergyman himself, must have been doubly strained by the loyal co-operation of this arch-enemy of the Church. The strain must have been greatly increased by the fact that Charles had himself received little but kindness from clergy. In particular, he owed an incalculable debt to his old friend Henslow at Cambridge, the more so as Henslow spared no trouble in helping him with his work after his return to England. (" Since my return Henslow has constantly rendered me every assistance which the kindest friend could offer.") But for the devoutly religious Henslow, he would never have been appointed to the *Beagle*. How could he now use the experience which he had gained through his friend's influence and kindness in order to join forces with a man who openly mocked at those who, like Henslow, were ordained ministers in the Church ? And what of his old captain and deeply religious friend FitzRoy ? Matters at home were no easier. Darwin's wife went regularly to church and took the Sacrament. She read the Bible with her children and had them baptized and confirmed in the Church of England. Though she did not talk much about the matter, Charles knew well enough that she suffered deeply because he did not share her faith. What was his duty to her ?

On the other side was the fact that co-operation with Huxley was essential, for without his help, the battle might be altogether lost : the *Origin* might go the way of the *Vestiges*. Charles was put to the test. It was a question of the praise of men or the praise of God, but he had already compromised himself so far that he could only choose the former.

To the end of his life, the old warfare continued in Darwin's mind. Try as he would, he could not escape from God. Gradually his emotional life atrophied under the strain of the battle. Religious feeling disappeared and with it much else beside. Shakespeare was " intolerably dull," he no longer took pleasure in pictures, in poetry, or even in music. The beauty of nature no longer thrilled him. The world became cold and dead. As we have already seen, even his reasoning powers became distorted when he dwelt upon subjects even remotely concerned with his conflict.

Finally the time came for Charles Darwin to die with the conflict still unresolved. Not long before this event the Duke of Argyle talked to him at his bedside. The Duke reminded him of how greatly Charles' own researches had increased the cogency of the arguments for natural theology. He pointed to the fertilization of orchids, the natural history of the earthworms and other wonderful contrivances in nature. Then he remarked that it was surely impossible to look at these without seeing that they were the effect and the expression of mind. " I shall never forget Darwin's answer," he wrote. " He looked at me very hard and said : ' Well, that often comes over me with overwhelming force, but at other times,' and he shook his head vaguely, adding, ' it seems to go away.' "

It is time to assess Darwin's influence on the world. What did he achieve ?

By 1840 all educated people in England accepted the main conclusions of the Bridgewater Treatises. The greatest scientists of the day—among them William Whewell, Sir Charles Bell, William Buckland and William Prout—had, at the invitation of the Royal Society, written learned volumes " on the Power, Wisdom and Goodness of God, as manifested in the Creation." It was hoped by some of the greatest leaders in scientific thought that before long " the volumes of Nature and Revelation " would be " simultaneously perused " in schools and colleges, " the two kindred seeds " being effectively sown in the minds of the young and growing into a deep and unshakable sense of gratitude and love to God. In this way, so it was hoped, vice and degradation would be removed from the land in a generation.[1]

At that time and, indeed, much later, men of science did not feel that it was out of place to mention God, even in strictly scientific memoirs. Daubeny's paper, read to the British Association in 1860, was deeply religious in tone. Lord Wrottesley, in his Presidential Address to the Association in the same year, after outlining the wonderful recent achievements of science, spoke of scientific research as " a glorious hymn to the Creator's praise." He told his hearers that to be indifferent " to the wonders around us " was a cause of " deep reproach, nay, almost a crime." It was our duty to investigate nature, " feeling assured that the more we thus exercise, and by exercising improve, our intellectual faculties, the more worthy shall we be, the better shall we be fitted to come nearer to our God."

Such quotations might be multiplied almost indefinitely The attitude of the day was one of deep reverence. If the dubious credit for emancipating scientific thought from theology must be given to any one man, that man was Darwin, helped, of course, by what Professor F. Wood

[1] Sir David Brewster, *Letters on Natural Magic*, 1832, p. 350. Brewster was President of the Royal Society.

Jones has called " the partisan pleadings . . . of Huxley and Haeckel."[1] For Darwin had treated the sacred subjects of man's body and man's mind without reference to religion. He found in science a way of escape from God. It was no wonder that his writings produced a sense of liberation in the minds of thousands of his contemporaries, for there were others, too, who wanted to escape, and they were delighted when they learned how it might be done.

In the early days those who took up science did so, for the most part, out of a reverent desire to think God's thoughts after Him. From Darwin's day onwards they often did so—as indeed they still do—out of a desire to escape from theology. For such, the very mention of God in connexion with scientific work, produces a feeling of disgust, even of resentment. The animosity and prejudice elicited show only too plainly that a secret conflict has been touched on the raw. Such men and women have entered science—professionally or as camp followers—in order to escape from God. When theology is mixed with science they begin to feel insecure, for their retreat is endangered and they react accordingly.

From Darwin's time onwards, Christians, seeing the pain which is caused by every mention of God in connexion with science, have been content to follow Darwin's lead. Rather than give offence, they have let science develop unmixed with religion. It is this fact, surely, that explains the " two-compartment mind " of many Christians. It arose through the misplaced courtesy of Christians in the world of science, who, rather than cause offence, decided to cease speaking of God in their scientific papers and to make their religion—just what Darwin wanted it to be—a private affair. Those who criticize men like Faraday, Clerk-Maxwell and Kelvin for keeping their science and religion in " idea-tight compartments " would do better to ask why they did so.

[1] *Design and Purpose*, 1942, p. 44.

CHAPTER VI

" GOOD SQUIB "

No sooner had he read the " origin of species " than Professor Sedgwick, the Cambridge geologist, at once recognized Darwin's motive in writing it. The book was, he said, " a dish of rank materialism cleverly cooked and served up merely to make us independent of a Creator." He ventured the prophecy, also, that if Darwin's teachings were accepted, humanity " would suffer a damage that might brutalize it, and sink the human race into a lower grade of degradation than any into which it has fallen since its written records tell us of its history "—a fear shared by Carlyle.

Charles Darwin himself, at times elated with enthusiasm, at others fearful of failure, was in no mood to consider these warnings objectively. To his friends, he merely referred to Sedgwick as a prejudiced " old bird " and no sooner had he heard that his book was selling well than he wrote to a friend saying that the sales would make " poor dear old Sedgwick groan." Later on, when a reviewer pointed out, quite bluntly, what Sedgwick had merely *implied*—namely, that Charles had shown every criminal how to justify his ways—Darwin mockingly referred to the accusation as a " good squib " and gave the matter no further thought.

The " squib," however, turned out to be a bomb, and certainly it was anything but " good." In time the theory of evolution permeated human thought in almost every direction and—as we shall shortly see—the ultimate result was exactly what Sedgwick had said it would be— brutalization.

The new doctrine very soon began to undermine religion

For Darwin himself, natural selection was, as we have already seen, an attempt to avoid the argument from design. Looked at through evolutionary spectacles, the natural world now became a scene of fierce struggle. That struggle formed part of the core of the universe. If at times nature seemed beautiful and tranquil, the evolutionist was not impressed. He supposed that beauty was a cruel deception. At bottom the world was ugly and it was hard to believe that it could have been ordained by a loving God. Perhaps, despite his reason, he still clung to his religion. But even so, the new ideas followed him remorselessly even into the House of God. As Beverley Nichols[1] has so well remarked, they created a suppressed psychological refrain to the Psalms and hymns.

O give thanks unto the Lord.
> Yes, but he put the mouse into the cat's paw.
For his mercy endureth for ever.
> Perhaps there are a million mice in a million cat's paws at this very moment.

The concept of struggle also affected biological thought profoundly. The older idea that nature was harmonious —that living things were adapted to one another—gave place to the idea that each individual and each group of individuals was battling against an environment to which it was ill-adapted. Every instance of a lack of adaptation, of what came to be called *dysteleology* was, therefore, seized upon as affording further evidence of universal struggle. Biologists looked for cruelty, for maladaptation, for useless organs. They spent whole lifetimes in the study of phenomena which seemed out of place in an intelligently planned world and, as the enormous volume of scientific literature grew in size, they came to imagine that their science represented nature as it really was. Hardly anyone noticed that the study of ecology, of organisms in relation

[1] *The Fool Hath Said*, 1936, p. 18.

to their surroundings, was being neglected. Yet, for
every instance of maladaptation in nature, there were a
thousand instances of adaptation near at hand concerning
which no memoirs were written and no interest aroused.

It is true that Darwin himself was by no means blind to
the real situation. At times, as his writings show quite
clearly, he appreciated the fact that examples of co-operation
in nature were common enough. Moreover, he did not
wish the expression " struggle for existence " to be understood in too literal a way : the word " struggle " was to
be thought of only " in a large and general sense." Yet,
far more often than not, Darwin forgot about co-operation
and saw only struggle, and he spoke of " struggle " in a
way that was, to say the least, crudely anthropomorphic.
His followers did likewise and but rarely remembered
their master's feebly uttered warnings.

For Darwin, even the buds of a tree were engaged in a
mad scramble to see which of them could best appropriate
the available supplies of sap. The same idea was later
carried to ludicrous extremes—with the warm support of
Darwin. Roux, in Germany, published a fantastic book
which he called *The Struggle of the Parts in the Organism*
(*Der Kampf der Theile im Organismus*, 1881). In this, he
maintained that the general shape and structure of organisms was determined by the struggle of the various cells
with one another. Just as the struggle of individual people
gave rise (under a *laissez-faire* regime) to the structure of
society, so the cells fighting and competing, produced
organisms. It was as simple as that !

In England Darwin, Romanes and others, hailed this as
a discovery of gigantic importance. It seemed to them
as if the Darwinian key was now about to unlock the
mysteries of physiology. (In time Darwin even imagined
molecules as engaged in the struggle.) This ill-considered
enthusiasm was, however, somewhat tempered by the
consideration that Herbert Spencer, an *Englishman*, had

thought of the same idea years before Roux, a fact that Roux had failed to notice.

To interpret nature as a struggle for existence, is certainly a *possible* procedure. When, as in civil war, the individuals involved are consciously and deliberately fighting for their existence, such a struggle is, of course, a literal fact. In all other cases it is a metaphor which owes its appeal to a suggestive analogy with human beings. In such cases the metaphor would often seem to be rather far-fetched, especially when the individuals involved do not know that they are struggling and have no idea that their struggle is for the sake of continued existence. When, for instance, we open a bottle of ginger beer, the dissolved carbon dioxide gas is liberated in limited amount and, if we like to think it so, an enormous multitude of small bubbles promptly start a life and death struggle for the gas, their only source of nutriment. Those that are unsuccessful in the struggle perish miserably, while those which are successful grow in size and eventually rise to the surface. Similar instances are met with in many other common phenomena—such as the production of crystals and the formation of rain. However, no one seems even to have suggested that the concept of struggle throws light on such phenomena as these, and, if anyone were to do so, it would probably be considered a joke. The reason why we do not take such suggestions seriously is simply that bubbles, raindrops and crystals do not *know* they are struggling and do not *wish* to survive longer than their fellows. Yet, precisely the same observations might be made about 99 per cent. of the cases to which the Darwinian formula has been seriously applied. The individuals, whatever they may be—buds on a tree, young fish in the sea, creeping, crawling caterpillars tempting birds to satiate " that hungry feeling "—know nothing whatever of the struggle in which they are supposed to be engaged. Unless, therefore, we are seriously prepared to use the struggle concept in such instances as that of the ginger beer, it would appear to be highly inconsistent to speak of a struggle at all. Indeed, nothing is more extraordinary than the fact that many who accuse Christians of " anthropomorphizing " nature when they speak of God, are perfectly prepared to accept the struggle theory of evolution.[1]

This is but one illustration of the way in which the evolution theory served to muddle human thinking. Outwardly, a new generation of materialists ridiculed Christianity for being anthropomorphic. They said that the Christian God had been made in the fashion of a man —a benevolent, grey-bearded, old gentleman sitting in the sky. But now it was time for humanity to do away with such childish conceits. They forthwith proceeded to make out that the power behind nature was not like men at their best, but like men at their worst—like individuals engaged in constant struggle with one another. And mother Nature herself was duly deprived of her grey beard in order to bring her up-to-date. But she was not dehumanized. She became like a fancier of pigeons (Darwin's own analogy), unerringly looking after those of her children best fitted to survive.

Even when creatures are conscious, the word " struggle " would appear to have little meaning as applied to evolution. Modern mathematical biologists (Haldane, Wright, etc.) have pointed out that a 1 per cent. advantage is sufficient in the so-called " struggle for existence." In such a contest, the individual would not notice any difference at all. No man would be any wiser if, by reason of the fact that he could run away slightly faster than his neighbour in presence of danger, he had a 1 per cent. less chance of

[1] The absurdity of the " struggle " doctrine is only matched by the absurdity of those orthodox evolutionists who profess to be able to " see through " it. Thus Dr. Chalmers Mitchell (*Evolution and the War*, 1915) remarks : " There is no bloodshed among plants, but there is overcrowding, crushing, starving, smothering, strangling." From this it would really seem as if a little blood-letting would be a welcome change !

being run over in the street. An animal would be none the wiser if it could get 1 per cent. more food than its neighbour, or have 1 per cent. more offspring. It is indeed astonishing how the word " struggle " has been allowed to remain in biological literature. Other anthropomorphic ideas of a similar nature, such as the explanation of chemical reactions in terms of the love and hate of atoms, are generally looked upon with mild amusement. It is difficult to resist the conclusion that the reason for this state of affairs is to be found simply in the fact that the conception of struggle is anti-theological in nature.

To all this it may be retorted that, after all, the controversy is largely a matter of words. Even though the word " struggle " may be somewhat of a misnomer it has come to stay and it is not understood too literally in academic circles.

Such a defence may satisfy those, only too often aloof from the world of affairs, who neither notice nor care about the harm their own ideas have done to society. Others will be less easily satisfied. The fact remains that the constant misuse of the word " struggle " first of all had the effect of making it difficult for the man in the street to trust in God's goodness and, after that, it caused Darwin's " good squib " to explode. With these preliminary remarks, we may pass on to consider some of the effects which the evolutionary theory has had upon history.

Hailed as one of the greatest discoveries of all time, it was inevitable that, sooner or later, evolution would exert an influence in realms other than biology. Nor were developments of this kind long in coming and, by now, it will hardly be necessary to add that, when they came, they received the warmest support from the biologists of the day.

The most important of these developments was in the realm of political and sociological thought.

Long before Darwin, Patrick Mathew had already

applied the principle of natural selection to politics.   He
had urged that the hereditary nobility in Europe ought to
be abolished since their continued existence was " an outrage " on nature's law of evolution—an outrage " which
she will not pass unavenged."   Decadence, he claimed,
was bound to set in when " no effort is needed on the part
of the nobility to protect their own, and no war to draw
forth or preserve their powers by exertion."

In 1869, ten years after the publication of the *Origin*,
there appeared a book by Walter Bagehot called *Physics and
Politics*.   In this the well-known author, the editor of the
Economist, attempted to work out the political implications
of Darwinism.   Though a brilliant man of letters in his day,
Bagehot's knowledge of science was so limited that apparently he did not even know the difference between physics
and biology—for the word " physics " in the title of the
book was clearly intended to mean " biology."   The book
sold well and was translated abroad where it had a great
influence.   Even to this day all writers on biology and
politics regard it as a classic.

According to Bagehot the principles of natural selection
apply to literature, to national characteristics, to nations
and so on, in the same way as they apply to organisms.
Conflict is of the utmost value in the destiny of a race.
Macaulay was only expressing biological truth when he
said that " many an army prospered under a bad commander,
but none ever did so under a debating society."   Strong
nations prevail over weak ones and, on the whole, the
strongest tend to be the best.   In wars, therefore, the
nation that wins is the nation that *ought* to win.

All this was set out in the dullest possible way—or
perhaps the fact is that, to-day, we have quite lost the art
of wading through endless verbose repetition with enjoyment.   Yet the author must have felt conscious of his lack
of inspiration when he wrote : " I am, I know, very long
and very tedious in setting out this. . . . "   Nevertheless,

later on, he was pleased enough when he received a translation of the book into Russian and, even more so, when the great Darwin himself became greatly interested in his ideas and received them favourably.

Best known of all writers of the day was Herbert Spencer, who applied evolutionary ideas to current problems in a ruthless and thorough-going fashion and eventually exerted an enormous influence. It was, in fact, very largely through Spencer's writings that Darwinism reached the man in the street, though Spencer must not, of course, be regarded as a mere popularizer of Darwin, for he had published his evolutionary views some years before Darwin had ventured to do so. Spencer saw the struggle for existence in every sphere of life. Evolutionary struggle was the great principle of nature which tried every man's work of what sort it was. If men " are sufficiently complete to live, they *do* live," he wrote, " and it is well they should live. If they are not sufficiently complete to live, they die, and it is best they should die " (*Social Statics*). His conviction that the struggle of nature ought not to be interfered with led him to oppose state-education, poor laws, regulation of housing conditions and, even, the protection of the ignorant from medical quacks. He believed too, that sanitary inspection and supervision was against nature's laws—unless, indeed, conditions became so bad as to imperil the community. No one who recognised biological truths, he said, would think of violating the principle of natural selection by the " artificial preservation of those least able to take care of themselves."

Spencer propounded these fantastic views with a self-assurance and certainty that knew no limits. Stories of his alleged infallibility circulated widely in scientific circles of the day and caused much amusement, but they did not reach the general public. It was said that he had replied to an argument : " That cannot be true for otherwise the *First Principles* would have to be re-written—and the edition is stereotyped." Even Darwin said that he felt like a worm when he read Spencer but, he added, that like the worm, he retained the privilege of wriggling.

Spencer applied evolution, not only to sociology, but to the entire cosmos. His fundamental evolutionary idea was that the " homogeneous " always turned into the " heterogenous," to which he added the law of the conservation of energy (which he always misnamed " force "). He made no serious attempt to master the physics of his day and his anxiety to prove that a diffuse gas, existing throughout space, would spontaneously evolve into the universe as we know it, led him to deny the law of the conservation of angular momentum and to imagine that hot and cold bodies could exist side by side for ever. Thus Spencer's " science " came into violent conflict with the established principles of physics. Yet, he dressed up his arguments with a persuasiveness and tact that deceived almost everyone save the professional physicists. On the one hand, he asserted that the universe needed no creation and could get along quite happily without God, which was just what the atheists wanted and, on the other, he artfully threw the sop to Christians by telling them that religion was concerned with the worship of the unknowable, and that science only dealt with the knowable, so that religion was for ever inviolable.

Spencer's books sold in enormous numbers. He succeeded, largely, because he was the first philosopher to write in a language which the masses could understand. Writers and scholars of the day greeted each succeeding book with howls of delight. F. A. P. Barnard, a well-known American writer, summarized the opinion of millions when he wrote : " We have in Herbert Spencer, not only the profoundest thinker of our time, but the most capacious and most powerful intellect of all time. . . . In all the history of science there is but one name which can be compared to his, and that is Newton's."

In America evolution soon became the rage. It reached the educated classes chiefly through the writings of Spencer and the masses through novels and popular journalism. As a contemporary writer remarked in the *Galaxy* : " Journalism is dyed so deep with it that the favourite logic of the leading articles is survival of the fittest, and the favourite jest is sexual selection."

Among American naturalists, Louis Agassiz was the only one who did not accept evolution in one form or another. He was convinced that it was a temporary " fad " but, when he died in 1873, evolutionary doctrines were at the height of their success and even his own pupils had left him for the opposing camp. Among those who were accounted the leaders in evolutionary thought was Asa Gray who for long maintained a correspondence with Darwin.

A number of naturalists in America, as well as in Europe, protested that evolution was in no way inimical to religion. Asa Gray reasserted constantly that Darwin had not undermined the arguments of Paley. His contention was that " natural selection . . . may be considered [as] one of the possible theories of the working of God's plan." He accepted evolution, not because he believed that it had been proved, but because " such a theory chimes in with the established doctrines of physical science [*sic*] and is not unlikely to be largely accepted before it can be proved." This opinion, which came to be widely held in educated circles throughout the world, was undoubtedly due to the influence of Spencer who, by his incredibly clever propaganda, succeeded in convincing nearly everyone that his theories were in no way opposed to the " established doctrines of physical science." If some well-known physicist of the day had been sufficiently gifted with the power of writing and speaking to explode this fiction, the triumph of evolution might have been far less spectacular than in fact it was.

Evolutionary views were welcomed with open arms by American industrialists. The great magnates saw in the absorption of smaller companies, an illustration of nature's law. James Hill, fighting to get the railways under his control, openly proclaimed that " the fortunes of railroad companies are determined by the law of the survival of the fittest." Andrew Carnegie was at first deeply troubled by the collapse of Christian theology and the un-Christian ways of big business. Morality, he believed, was being undermined. In the end, however, evolutionary propaganda set his mind at rest by enabling him to see right and wrong in a new light. Having once mastered Herbert Spencer, he felt no further need to concern himself with the sins which big business committed against its vanquished competitors. For, after all, the law of competition was biological. " It is here," said Carnegie, " we cannot evade it. . . . While the law may sometimes be hard for the individual, it is best for the race "—so the true Christian duty was to apply it in all its ruthlessness. J. D. Rockefeller also, who accumulated mountains of wealth by methods that were the scandal of the day, defended his conduct in the same way. In the course of a Sunday School address he is reported to have said : " The growth of large business is merely the survival of the fittest. . . . The American Beauty rose can be produced in the splendour and fragrance which bring cheer to its beholder only by sacrificing the early buds which grow up around it. This is not an evil tendency in business. It is merely the working out of a law of nature and a law of God."

Evolution, in short, gave the doer of evil a respite from his conscience. The most unscrupulous behaviour towards a competitor could now be rationalized : evil could be called good. Sumner, who came to be called the Darwin of the Social Sciences, put the new doctrine very well when he claimed that " while men were fighting for glory and greed, for revenge and superstition, they were building human society."[1]

[1] *Sumner To-day. Selected Essays of W. G. Sumner*, 1940, p. 126.

Not only did the doctrine of evolution enable the doer of evil to justify his conduct by claiming that evil was good but, even when evil was blatant and admitted, it effectively paralysed the will to reform. The spirit that crept over the American continent is well epitomized by the story of a conversation that took place between Youmans and Henry George. The former had fervently denounced the political corruptions of New York. "What do you propose to do about it?" asked Henry George. "Nothing! . . . it's all a matter of evolution," said his friend, "We can only wait for evolution. Perhaps in four or five thousand years evolution may have carried men beyond this state of things."

By the end of the century, as a result of the acute misery caused by industrial depression and social unrest, the application of evolution to sociology had been discredited. As Hofstadter[1] puts it, the middle classes now fled from the hideous image of rampant competitive brutality. Spencer lived to see his popularity wane. A new generation laconically turned the pages of his books wondering, above all else, how their elders had ever had the patience to wade through such seas of rubbish. In the early 1900's William James, lecturing to his students, made a point of pouring the utmost scorn upon all that Spencer had taught. Spencer's "persistence of thought" was now declared to be "vagueness incarnate" while the great philosopher's notions of the "rhythm of motion" were facetiously illustrated by mocking references to rocking chairs. Truly, "the fashion of this world passeth away."[2]

Yet there was no change of heart. None, save the long-discredited Fundamentalists, seemed to discern that the trouble lay in the doctrine of evolution itself—or in Darwin's version of it. Mankind was infinitely the poorer

[1] R. Hofstadter, *Social Darwinism in American Thought* (1860–1915), 1945. References to statements made in the text will be found in this scholarly work.
[2] I Corinthians 7 : 31.

for having applied Darwinism to current affairs. Clearly a mistake had been made. William James and others like him suggested that the root error was the idea, latent in Spencerism, that man was powerless, a helpless puppet, in the drama of evolution. This must be corrected. Man must no longer accept his fate but must actively set to work to control his evolution. And so, not only in America, but throughout the world, new movements were set on foot. One of these was eugenics—the deliberate attempt to help nature to select the fittest. It was received with enormous enthusiasm in the years before the first world war and, captivated by evolutionary propaganda, many states passed sterilization laws. It need hardly be added that the law makers invariably assumed that rich people were better fitted to survive than poor people, so that the laws were framed for the doubtful benefit of the former alone. Eugenics has now passed its zenith but it was effectively applied in Hitler's Germany.

Before returning to these later developments, we must now go back in time once more and examine the effect of evolutionary teaching on the continent of Europe.

There have been wars all down history but never until the days of Darwin and Bagehot was it widely supposed that wars were desirable. The tyrants of old time often did wrong when they felt an inclination to do so, but the extent to which they were prepared to go was often seriously curbed by the thought that they would one day have to give account of their deeds at the Great Assize. In his book *Grey Eminence* Aldous Huxley has reminded us of the case of Marie de Medicis, the Queen Mother, who in 1620 gave orders that her infantry might sack Angers before returning south. Father Joseph of Paris at once went to the old woman and told her that if she did not countermand the order she would without doubt be damned everlastingly. She was heartless, cruel and obstinate. No other threat would have touched her, but this threat most

certainly did.   Angers was saved.   The fear of hell may well
be—as, indeed, it undoubtedly is—a thoroughly bad motive
for going good, but however much moderns may despise it a
bad motive is a great deal better than no motive at all.   The
old-fashioned theology at least provided a restraint to evil.

The new evolutionary doctrines at once provided the
worst of mankind with an escape from their one remaining
restraint.   Darwin had shown how science could be used
as an escape from theology and he showed how every
worker of evil could justify his ways.

Nor was the world at all slow to learn the lesson.   If,
in the under-developed American continent, Darwinism
encouraged the unscrupulous practices of big business,
in countries where a strong militaristic clique existed, it
encouraged war.   Its influence, was, indeed, enormous and
world wide.   Darwin's books were translated into all the
main languages on earth—including Spanish, Czech, Polish,
Russian, Hebrew and even Japanese.   The ruling classes
seized upon them as representing the last word in science and
Darwinian catchwords were bandied to and fro by those
who could not get their way except by graft and intrigue.
The desire for peaceful settlements largely disappeared.

The effects of evolutionary teaching on the German mind
were almost unbelievable.   Sir Archibald Geikie,[1] who was
travelling in Austria in 1868–9 remarks : " what specially
struck me was the universal sway which the writings of
Darwin now exercises over the German mind."   A well-
known physician in Vienna remarked to him : " You are still
discussing in England whether or not the theory of Darwin
is true.   We have got a long way beyond that stage here.
His theory is now our common starting point."

The 43rd meeting of the German Naturalists and
Physicians (not unlike the British Association in England),
held at Innsbrück in 1868, was marked says Geikie, by an
astonishing liberty of expression, often amounting to " mere

[1] See *Nature*, 1869, Vol. I, Nov. 4, p. 22.

wanton defiance of the popular creed. Yet it was always received with applause." Karl Vogt, in particular, was outrageously profane, speaking in a manner " such as no man, not even the most free-thinking, would venture publicly to express " in England, and was greeted with thunderous applause. The new temper was due, as a German doctor put it, to the influence of two Englishmen —Charles Darwin and George Combe.[1]

Whether or no Bismarck was influenced by Darwinism in deciding on his wars of aggression I have been unable to discover. It is likely enough. The Empress of Prussia, daughter of Queen Victoria, was on intimate terms with Bismarck, though she refused to become his pawn. She had married Frederick of Prussia in 1858. The rising tide of unbelief in the Bible—Darwin, Colenso, Renan, Strauss, the Tübingen school—soon undermined her faith. She abandoned Christianity and " a time of unhappiness and spiritual disquiet " followed. Sir Charles Lyell spent the Christmas of 1864 in Berlin and found that the Empress had read Darwin carefully more than once and had absorbed his doctrines with great enthusiasm.[2]

Even at that early date the politics of at least one country were dominated by Darwin. In 1866 after the disastrous termination of the war with Prussia, the Austrian parliament assembled to discuss the reconsolidation of the Empire. A distinguished member of the Upper House began an important speech with the words : " The question we have first to consider is whether Charles Darwin is right or no." The Empire was in distress. Its politicians were concerned with reconstruction but were so infatuated with the new science that they were determined, first of all, to study Darwin so that the measures they took should be based on sound biological principles. Even in England the same

[1] A phrenologist who lectured in Heidelberg, etc. Phrenology was enthusiastically supported by nineteenth-century materialists. See, for example, A. Post, *Popular Freethought in America*, 1943.
[2] See E. E. P. Tisdall, *She Made World Chaos*, 1940, p. 201.

outlook was not unknown. A leading article in *Nature*[1] urged the Government to reconstruct the laws of this country so that they would assist the fittest to survive. The same article attributed England's greatness to the fact that, in the past, some of the laws of the country had, quite by chance, been constructed on Darwinian lines.

Nietzsche was much influenced by Darwin, though, as in so many other instances, it is believed that he gained his knowledge of evolution at second hand only. He accepts the theory of evolutionary struggle wholeheartedly, but he disapproves of Darwin for not carrying his ideas to their logical conclusion. He complains that Darwin's treatment of evolution " is no call for battle to prepare the earth for the Superman, but a sedative belief that the process of evolution will take care of itself, that our environment is automatically turning out better men, that natural selection is still going on." Darwin, he thought, failed to be logical because he was not, personally, an aristocrat. As a result the English were quite unable to see the full grandeur of evolution. As for Christianity, it was to be opposed vigorously, for it was unbiological in nature. " Christianity is the reverse of the principle of selection. If the degenerate and the sick man (the Christian) is to be of the same value as the healthy man (the pagan) . . . the natural course of evolution is thwarted and the unnatural becomes law[2].

The early effects of evolutionary teaching boded no good for the future. Native races, in particular, have no cause to feel grateful to Charles Darwin for, with the coming of evolution, the old desires for conciliation disappeared and the supposedly civilized world carried on wars of extermination unparalleled in history for their crass brutality. The monstrous affair of the Belgian Congo alone,

[1] 1860, Vol. I, p. 183 (Dec. 16).
[2] For full quotations and references see Crane Brinton, *Nietzsche*, 1941, p. 145 ff.

in the early years of our century, involved the slaughter of perhaps two or three times as many human beings as the first world war, which still looms so inordinately large in the thoughts of Europeans. Mass murder ? Well, and why not ? It was only a matter of the working of evolution. It went to prove that Europeans were the fittest to survive and they forthwith proceeded to pat themselves on the back and to look for new outlets to prove to themselves that they were the finest and best in all creation. " No one," says Barzun[1], " who has not waded through some sizeable part of the literature of the period 1870 to 1914 has any conception of the extent to which it is one long call for blood." And of course that call for blood was conducted in the " scientific " evolutionary jargon of the day. Peace was not even desired. Gladiatorial strife was by far the easiest way of settling international affairs —especially affairs with naked savages who had no weapons more dangerous than bows and arrows.

In Germany Haeckel wanted to found a religion based upon evolution. This was to be taught in schools instead of Christianity. His conception of evolution did away with a Creator altogether—for Darwin's doctrine was applied not only to living matter but to dead, to the origin of life itself. In some queer way or other the survival of the fittest among pieces of dead matter was supposed to make them live.

Rationalists received Haeckel's outpourings with enthusiasm not only in Germany but, eventually, in England also. Virchow, a well-known German biologist, was vigorously attacked—being called an anti-evolutionary obscurantist— simply because he insisted that Darwinism was *not* concerned with how lifeless matter became alive in the first place.

Throughout the civilized world politicians, right and left, claimed a monopoly in applying the principles of evolution. Marxism, in particular, owes much to evolutionary teaching. Karl Marx read the *Origin* in 1860 and

[1] J. M. Barzun, *Darwin, Marx and Wagner*, 1942, p. 100.

wrote : " Darwin's book is very important and serves me as a basis in natural science for the struggle in history." He sought permission to dedicate his world-famous book, *Das Kapital*, to Charles Darwin, a proposal to which Darwin would not agree. In years to come the books of Darwin, Spencer and Marx stood side by side on left-wing bookstalls, while the pamphlets of the political revolutionaries were suitably adorned with spicy quotations from the works of the first two authors.

Like the right-wing politicians, the revolutionary socialists saw in evolution a way of stifling their consciences. The new doctrine justified men in struggling for their rights—even though the struggle involved a denial of the Christian virtues. For it was against the law of nature that the poor should continue in their inferior position ; the cosmic process demanded that they should rise, rebel and fight for their rights, either to conquer or to perish in the attempt.

Such views created mistrusts and hatred throughout Europe. One of the worst features of Marxism is its all-pervading denial of any higher motives in man. For Marx, everything a rich man did, he did for ulterior motives. Even thought was not exempt—for his thoughts were a mere reflection of his economic condition. Here, again, Marx carried to its logical extreme the teaching of Darwin. It seemed only natural that each class of society should evolve its opinions along the line that made it best fitted to survive. There was no place for change of heart—if such apparent changes took place, they must be interpreted as stages in the sordid evolutionary process.

If evolutionary teaching stirred the workers to rebellion, it likewise confirmed the privileged classes in their determination to keep the workers in their place. For reason was just as much on their side. Thus, in 1877, two attempts were made to murder the German Emperor. The German press put the blame on the doctrine of evolution which was encouraging the discontented elements in society to rebel. Ernst Haeckel[1] at once proceeded to defend evolution against this calumny. After telling the usual story of a " cruel and merciless struggle for existence raging throughout all living nature," a tragic state of affairs which we can neither controvert nor change, but which inevitably results in the fact that a small " and chosen minority " can alone exist and flourish, he asserted with complete self-assurance that those who survived were not only the fittest to survive, but " the best." This completely disproved socialism. " Socialism demands equal rights, equal duties, equal possessions, equal enjoy- ments for every citizen alike, the theory of descent proves in exact opposition to this, that the realization of this de- mand is a pure impossibility." Indeed, he concluded, " every reasonable and unprejudiced politician " ought to encourage the teaching of evolution in schools as an antidote to social- ism! What the working man, his constitution undermined by semi-starvation while the sickly, coddled child of wealth had food enough and to spare, would have thought of these arguments, Haeckel did not stop to consider.

There is no space here even to outline the subsequent history of evolutionary thought up to our own day ; but it has remained true to type. In England, the turn of the century saw Karl Pearson writing : " You may hope for a time when the sword shall be turned into the plowshare . . . but, believe me, when that day comes, man will no longer progress," while, in Germany, Prince Bülow, later German Chancellor, was saying : " We must realize that there is no such thing as permanent peace, and must re- member Moltke's words : ' Permanent peace is a dream, and not even a beautiful one, but war is an essential element of God's scheme of the world.' "[2]

[1] E. Haeckel, *Freedom in Science and Teaching*, 1879, pp. 91, 93.
[2] Quoted by C. J. H. Hayes, *A Generation of Materialism*, 1941, p. 340. In this book, and in that of J. M. Barzun (*op. cit.*) much further information on the effects of evolutionary thought upon politics will be found.

Our own generation has lived to see the inevitable result of evolutionary teaching—the result that Sedgwick foresaw as soon as he had read the *Origin*. Mussolini's attitude was completely dominated by evolution. In public utterances, he repeatedly used the Darwinian catchwords while he mocked at perpetual peace, lest it should hinder the evolutionary process. For him, the reluctance of England to engage in war only proved the evolutionary decadence of the British Empire.

In Germany it was the same. Adolf Hitler's mind was captivated by evolutionary teaching—probably since the time he was a boy. Evolutionary ideas—quite undisguised—lie at the basis of all that is worst in *Mein Kampf* —and in his public speeches. A few quotations, taken at random, will show how Hitler reasoned. In a speech at Nuremberg, in 1933, he argued that a higher race would always conquer a lower. " Thus there results the subjection of a number of people under the will, often of only a few persons, a subjection based simply upon the right of the stronger, a right which, as we see it in Nature, can be regarded as the sole conceivable right, because it is founded on reason." He went on to explain that it was for this reason that he hated communism. " For communism is not a higher stage of development ; rather it is the most primitive form of life—the starting-point."

Hitler's hatred of the Jews was rationalized in the same way. The Germans were the higher race, destined for a glorious evolutionary future. For this reason it was essential that the Jews should be segregated, otherwise mixed marriages would take place. Were this to happen, all nature's efforts " to establish an evolutionary higher stage of being may thus be rendered futile " (*Mein Kampf*).

Hitler's attitude to the League of Nations and to peace and war were based upon the same principles. " A world-court without a world police would be a joke . . . the whole world of Nature is a mighty struggle between strength and weakness—an eternal victory of the strong

over the weak. There would be nothing but decay in
the whole of nature if this were not so. States which
should offend against this elementary law would fall into
decay." In those early days Hitler himself was alarmed
to see signs of such decay in the German nation and was
confident that God had raised him up to save his country.
(Speech at Munich, 1923.) "He who would live must fight.
He who does not wish to fight in this world where permanent struggle is the law of life, has not the right to exist."
To think otherwise is to "insult" nature. "Distress, misery
and disease are her rejoinders" (*Mein Kampf*).[1]

Evolutionary views were drilled into the German people.
Germans were told they must suffer but that, when the
day of victory came, they would be rewarded at the cost
of conquered peoples. As a German writer puts it :
"To those Germans whose conscience was disturbed by
these promises, Darwin's materialistic doctrine of the
struggle of species was expounded. Since all natural
history was simply a struggle for the survival of the fittest,
any trick or ruse was permissible in order to facilitate the
victory of one's own species. Politics became an art and
a science beyond good and evil. Immorality, craftiness,
ruthlessness and brutality towards other nations were
raised to the level of virtues."[2]

In the schools it was the same. Biology was deliberately
taught with an evolutionary bias. In *No Retreat* (1943)
Anna Rauschning has given a vivid picture of how, at
school, her own children were stuffed with anecdotes to
show that the strong rightfully triumphed over the weak,
of how the spider rightfully devoured the fly, no mercy
ever being asked or given. The film *Snow White and the
Seven Dwarfs* was vilified because it glorified misshapen

[1] These quotations are taken from the unexpurgated English translation of *Mein Kampf* (Hutchinson, 1942) and from *Hitler's Speeches*,
2 vols., U.S.A., 1942. Reference may also be made to M. Oakeshott's
Social and Political Doctrines of Contemporary Europe, 1939.
[2] From *After Nazism—Democracy ?* Symposium by four Germans,
1945, p. 171.

human beings who ought to have been sent to death in the "Hitler chamber." The German Youth Movement agreed with the official view that the State has no right to support the struggles of the weak; for the individual must be sacrificed for the sake of the race. Later, during the war, evolutionary teaching was put into practice first by the murder of those in asylums and institutions and, later, of the supposedly inferior gypsies and Jews.

Such is the background to the Third Reich. Yet few things are more astonishing than the persistent attempts to hide the facts from the English speaking public. Volume after volume has poured from the publishing houses describing every phase of the Hitler régime, but their writers are so timidly afraid of being classed as anti-evolutionary "fundamentalists" that one may search through their books by the score (this is *not* an exaggeration) and scarcely find a mention of evolution or Charles Darwin. Numerous books on race and racism have also appeared in which evolution is, once again, either not mentioned at all or severely kept in the background.

In Russia Darwinism took an equally sinister form. In the West it had been invoked in the struggle between the "fit" rich and the "unfit" poor, or between the "have" and the "have-not" nations; in Russia it was a question of the evolutionary triumph of the proletariat against the capitalists. The inhuman atrocities connected with the October Revolution and the later collectivisation of the farms were carried out in the name of science. Courses on Darwinism were given at Universities, and popular lectures to the workers, while, in World War II, systematic compulsory lectures on Darwinism were given, even to prisoners of war, as a former Polish prisoner himself informed the writer. After constant indoctrination of this kind it becomes easier to understand the lack of feeling, and the scientific detachment which became characteristic of many Russian soldiers. Even the horrors of the Hitler camps are hardly as terrible as the revelations in *The Dark Side of the Moon*.[1]   The author, who has spent years investigating every extant report of the deportation of the Poles, has himself been morally shattered by his findings. For weeks on end human beings were kept in cattle trucks by soldiers who, though overbearing and rough, were not vindictive or passionate. Yet scarcely an instance can be found in which these men showed one spark of humanity. Indeed, no savages on earth have ever sunk so low as persistently to refuse water to those who were neither captives nor enemies—and to refuse not out of malice but simply because they could not be bothered to do otherwise. "This question has occupied me profoundly," says the Polish writer. "Throughout my work on this book, work which has occupied several years, I have searched the evidence exhaustively on this point. I have also put the question to every single person with whom I have talked. It has been of immense importance to me, of an importance greater than I can possibly express, to discover that some instinct of humanity did survive, somehow. The answer invariably given me has been that it did not."

Our thoughts go back to what that " old bird " Sedgwick said. Is this the final outcome of what Charles Darwin so mockingly called a " good squib " ?

There have, of course, been a number of erudite attempts to show that the disastrous effects of the doctrine of evolution upon the world were merely due to a misunderstanding of the scientific theory and that, if only the latter had been properly understood, no such results would have followed. However, their authors generally give their case away without noticing the fact. H. F. Osborn, for example, after candidly admitting that human decadence " is partly due to a complete misunderstanding of creative evolution," proceeds to sing the praises of teleology like a bird. He then attempts to show that, when evolution is correctly

---

[1] Published by Faber, 1946. Preface by T. S. Eliot.

understood, it encourages people to be good. "The moral principle inherent in evolution," he says, "is that nothing can be gained in this world without effort; the ethical principle inherent in evolution is that only the best has a right to survive."[1] The first of these statements is totally false, un-Christian, and indeed, anti-Christian. The basis of Christ's teaching is that God treats people in a way that they do *not* deserve and that man must treat his fellows likewise. Effort may achieve much that is good, but the highest and best things—forgiveness, love, God's gifts in nature, peace of mind and fellowship with God—are exactly the things that we can never earn by effort. If we cannot take them as gifts, *unearned*, we must for ever do without them. As for the second statement—"that only the best has a right to survive" —it would no doubt have been warmly endorsed by Herr Hitler at the inception of his euthanasia campaign. Those who draw morals of this kind from evolution have no right to complain when others "misunderstand" Darwinism.

More recently, belated attempts[2] have been made to show that Mussolini and Hitler misunderstood evolution. It is said that they misinterpreted the concept of "race" and that Hitler, in particular, ignored the phenomenon of hybrid vigour.

We may agree entirely that modern science gives no support to the crude racial teaching of the pre-war dictators. Nevertheless, as Sir Arthur Keith has reminded us in his *Essays on Evolution*, it was Darwin himself who taught that evolution proceeds through war and struggle between isolated clans. It seems hardly fair, therefore, to blame foreign politicians for their "misinterpretations" of biological science.

The plain fact is that neither Darwin himself, nor his followers, can be exonerated from blame for even the

[1] H. F. Osborn, *Evolution and Religion in Education*, N.Y., 1926. p. 48.
[2] e.g., J. Needham, *History is on Our Side*, 1946.

worst results of evolutionary teaching. Although he would argue at times that moral qualities were " highly beneficial to the species " and had been developed by natural selection, yet at other times Darwin often said quite as plainly that it was wrong to ameliorate the conditions of the poor, since to do so would hinder the evolutionary struggle for existence.

Darwin also disapproved of the " prevention of over-multiplication " of the human species, since this would tend to hinder the selection of the best in the struggle for existence. It was Darwin, too, who could conceive of nothing more terrible than a decline of the birth rate in Britain because, in the end, this might mean that the English would no longer be in a position to continue to colonize the world. The importance of such colonization, he claimed, was beyond exaggeration. We can scarcely deny Hitler's claim to be a good Darwinian, seeing that he held similar views about his own nation.

It is true that Darwin did not himself carry his theories of struggle into practice, but was a kindly man and a good father. It is largely this fact that has for so long preserved his memory from criticism. But the moderns cannot have it both ways. For a long time now the world has been only too full of rich men who draw large incomes from the white slave traffic, from exploitation of natives in mines and factories, from selling arms to small nations after deliberately stirring up war and so on. Such men are often clean living and kindly in their private lives and make excellent fathers. For, as Christ pointed out, even evil men know how to give good gifts to their children. Such people are, however, generally regarded as execrable hypocrites by left-wing sympathizers, particularly if (as is, no doubt, occasionally the case) they make profession of Christianity. Yet Darwin (and Spencer, too, for that matter), who made substantial sums of money by the sale of books which spread an immoral and false philosophy,

is regarded as immune from criticism because of his private
life.   And this, despite the fact that he probably did as
much harm as all the private manufacturers of armaments
ever did and, even, provided them with a philosophy to
justify their ways.   Clearly no half measures are permissible.   Either we may condemn Darwin, together with all
others who have profited by the misery they have caused
to others, or else we may judge people by their private
lives alone and think charitably of all men.   It will not
do to pick and choose.

Attention must be drawn to one further matter before
bringing this chapter to a close.   In the last few years a
slowly dawning realization of the enormous harm that
evolutionary teaching has done, has inspired a number of
writers to attempt to base morality on biology.   It has
been stated that man's duty is to help evolution forward,
and C. H. Waddington has argued that evolution now
enables us to give an exact definition to the terms *right*
and *wrong*—right being that which helps and wrong that
which hinders evolution.

These arguments are a rehash of late nineteenth century
teaching—not a single new point having emerged.   They
are far-fetched, unconvincing, academic in the extreme and
unlikely to inspire anyone outside a narrow intellectual
circle.   The false reasoning involved in attempts to build
ethics upon an evolutionary basis has recently been exposed
in a devastating manner by W. F. Quillian [1] who has traced
all such attempts back to their source.   The fact that
attempts of this kind should have been made at all, is a
matter of absorbing psychological interest—evolution has
become so fashionable that public and scholars alike are
sometimes prepared to go to extremes of illogicality so long as
their " evolutionary outlook " is not imperilled.   But, fascinating as the subject is, there is no space to discuss it here.

---

[1] *The Moral Theory of Evolutionary Naturalism*, 1945.

CHAPTER VII

EVOLUTION AND BIOLOGICAL SCIENCE

THE IMMEDIATE EFFECT OF DARWINISM WAS TO stimulate biological research. Yet this stimulation, for which evolution has received so much credit, was by no means always of a healthy character. On the whole, naturalists were driven into laboratories instead of into the fields. They spent their time constructing " family trees," instead of discovering how animals lived. Organisms came to be thought of as isolated units divorced from their surroundings and the study of *ecology*, the study of the organism in relation to its surroundings, which had formed a large part of the older natural history, was now sadly neglected.

The Darwinians, as we have seen, looked upon nature as a sphere of struggle. They could think only of animals red in tooth and claw. They ceased to see the world as a harmonious whole, in which each unit had its place, and they thought of it instead as a nightmare of disharmony and chaos. Whereas an older generation of natural historians had looked for design or *teleology*, the newer generation of biologists began, quite deliberately, to look for the *absence* of design, for what they pleased to call *dysteleology*. As a result, biology became, very largely, the study of misfits. Even man himself, as Wood Jones amusingly remarks, came to be regarded as the miscarriage of an ape.

One way in which the new temper showed itself, was in the study of useless organs. Anatomists were never more delighted than when they could point to some newly discovered useless organ—clear record of an earlier stage of evolution and but one further convincing proof that evolution had actually occurred. The obvious fact, pointed out by T. H. Huxley, that each one of these new arguments for evolution only served to make the Darwinian theory less and less plausible, was conveniently overlooked. For, if useless organs really remain for enormous periods of time, despite natural selection, it is only possible to conclude that natural selection does not operate at all or that, if it does, it works so slowly that its creative and adaptive powers must be very limited indeed. In this case it could scarcely have been an important factor in the production of species.

In other ways, too, the development of biological science was seriously hindered. Recent researches in psychology have confirmed what has long been suspected—that, when the human mind has once looked upon a problem in one particular light, other equally valid ways of looking at that problem become " blocked."[1]   The mind, in short, very easily becomes one-tracked. This is exactly what happened in the case of Darwinism, a fact which is, indeed, now widely recognized. No single way of regarding nature is fully comprehensive. Nature undoubtedly *is* built up of units of life—cells, plants, animals. Struggle and cruelty do occasionally enter into the relationships between the individuals of the last named group. But the recognition of this fact is certainly no reason for ignoring a much more fundamental fact about nature. Taken widely, nature is a harmonious whole. Even the predators and preyed-upon form parts of that whole, their numbers being nicely balanced, so that one group rarely or never exterminates another. Thus the parasite never completely destroys its host species, or it would destroy itself also. Again, despite fearful exceptions in the case of mankind, serious inconvenience caused by parasites is relatively rare —thus the wild game of Africa harbour the malaria parasite

---

[1] For example, a person who has once seen a figure outlined in dots upon a piece of paper, now finds it much more difficult to see another figure that may be outlined equally clearly among the same dots.

without inconvenience to themselves. But in any case symbiotic union—union of two species for the benefit of both—is much more frequently encountered than parasitism.

Again, taken as a whole, the " struggle " for existence would appear to be merciful rather than cruel. Birds and animals which, by reason of old age or accident, have become unable to look for food and to enjoy life to the full, would suffer very greatly if they were simply left to die of starvation. As it is, they are generally mercifully and quickly delivered as soon as their powers fail, in addition to which they provide food for the predators. During the period of active health animals do not fear that they may be killed by their enemies—if they have any psychological feelings on the subject at all, it would seem that they are chiefly ones of enjoyment and pride in the fact that they are too smart for their foes. In the same way, a healthy man knows that motor cars are potentially very dangerous ; they are in fact his " natural enemies." But he does not fear that they will kill him as he crosses the road, for he takes a natural pride in the fact that he is skilful in avoiding danger. It may be that rabbits and birds look upon dogs and cats in much the same light !

To return to our theme, biologists who were hypnotized by the Darwinian interpretation of nature, professed to see nothing but waste on every side. Acorns that never turned into oak trees were wasted ; fishes that were eaten up by larger fishes, leaving only one or two survivors out of a million were wasted ; pollen that failed to fertilize flowers was wasted, and so *ad infinitum*.

Waste formed the greatest of all arguments for disharmony in nature. It scarcely dawned upon the minds of the Darwinians that the material of seeds and eggs was not wasted at all, but formed nutritious meals for animals, birds and insects. The whole fallacy lay in the assumption that the *only* purpose of acorns was to produce oak trees, of fish eggs to produce adult fishes and so on. Yet the facts scarcely warrant this assumption. Indeed, no one who buys hens' eggs in a shop imagines that the eggs will be wasted if they do not turn into chickens !

The narrowness of outlook engendered by Darwinism greatly hindered early attempts to understand morphology. In Germany, Wilhelm His spent a large part of his life seeking to find out what happened as an embryo developed. How did new form come into being ? To-day he is universally regarded as a pioneer in this field of study yet, in his own time, he had to contend with merciless ridicule, especially from Haeckel. He was bluntly told " that we have better things to do in embryology than to discuss the tensions of germinal layers and similar questions, since all explanations must of necessity be of a phylogenetic nature." In other words, it was useless to discuss why an embryo was passing through a certain stage, if you could imagine that the stage it was passing through bore some resemblance to· an hypothetical ancestral fish. He well remarked that " this opposition to the application of the fundamental principles of science to embryology would scarcely be intelligible had it not a dogmatic background. No other explanation of living things is allowed than heredity, and any which is founded on another basis is rejected. The present fashion requires that even the smallest and most indifferent enquiry must be dressed in a phylogenetic costume, and whilst, in former ages, authors professed to read in every detail some intention of ·the *Creator Mundi* modern scientists have the aspiration to pick out from every occasional observation a fragment of the ancestral history of the living world." Finally, he concludes : " To think that heredity will build organic beings without mechanical means is a bit of unscientific mysticism."[1]

In addition to its harmful influence on the development of morphology, Darwinism was almost certainly responsible

[1] W. His, *Proc. Roy. Soc., Edin.*, 1888, **15**, 287.

for the neglect of Mendel's classic work on heredity. This, at any rate, was the contention of Bateson, though more recently Fisher has charged Bateson with being a " zealous partisan " in the matter.[1] Fisher argues that Mendel did not really oppose evolution and may even have regarded it favourably. So, for that matter, did His. Moreover, he argues that Bateson was wrong in claiming that Darwin was responsible for a decline in breeding research. All this may very well be the case, nevertheless everybody knows that Mendel's work *was* neglected and, seeing how important it was and that it was published in a well-known journal of the day, it is difficult to believe that the Darwinian partisans should take no share of blame. Mendel's work proved conclusively that the apparent " chance variations " by which Darwin had set so much store were predictable and that they could not have helped in the formation of new species. Knowing as we do how narrow minded they were, is it likely that Darwinians would have welcomed such a discovery ?

It is commonly said that Darwin was practically responsible for creating modern biology. Certainly he did exceedingly valuable work both in proving the close connexion between nearly related species, and also in his study of crustacea, fertilization, earthworms and so on. Yet the influence of his theory of natural selection, even in biology, probably did more harm than good. Though it stimulated the writing of innumerable scientific memoirs, most of these were concerned with trivialities which did little or nothing to increase man's fundamental understanding of the world around him. Indeed, by concentrating attention on the small changes which structures such as teeth and sea shells had undergone over long periods of time, they diverted attention from the amazing fact that such structures have come into existence at all.

Far from being dead in the 1880's, the attitude of which

[1] R. A. Fisher, *Annals of Science*, 1936, Vol. I, p. 115.

His complained is still very much alive to-day; for the influence of Darwinism has obscured the fact that evolution is first and foremost a *chemical* problem. Living creatures are not built up out of heredity, or natural selection or struggle for existence, nor out of any other biological catch-words, they are built up out of chemical molecules. Of course, it may be held that this is not the whole story, and that there is, so to speak, a spiritual constituent in addition to matter, but, whatever the truth about this may be, it is clear that from the standpoint of materialistic science, it is the matter alone that counts. For the materialist, therefore, organisms are limited by the properties of atoms and molecules. Somehow or other, he must explain how chemical molecules of gigantic complexity came into existence and have been able to arrange themselves in increasingly complicated ways. This is the fundamental problem of evolution, yet it is generally ignored in modern books on the subject, nor, (at least to the author's knowledge) has the problem ever been fairly faced.

The astonishing way in which evolutionary doctrines blind their devotees to the real issue at stake is well shown by the attitude which both Darwin himself and his followers ever since have adopted towards matter. Among superstitious peoples the belief is commonly encountered that matter is in some way linked up with human desires. It is supposed to be able to mould itself in accordance with human wishes, provided only that people wish hard enough ! Now this, astonishing as it may seem, is not dissimilar to the attitude of Darwin himself. Darwin seems to have thought that whenever animals needed some new organ, it would automatically turn up. In other words, a need or wish for eyes with which to see, itself, in some mysterious way arranged and joined chemical molecules together until the desired organ was created. Darwin was equally superstitious about the formation of instincts. He believed that they, like organs of sight and hearing, were simply caused " by modifcations or variations in the brain, which we in our ignorance most improperly call spontaneous or accidental." [1]   He supposed that a mere need for these instincts would automatically bring them into existence.

Exactly the same attitude is found among modern evolutionary writers.   Thus Sir Arthur Keith assures his readers that " in evolution, the vitalizing, the creative power, acts from within, it is an inherent property of living matter . . . we have no knowledge of any kind of living matter that has not this creative power." [2]   Similarly, in his *Essays on Human Evolution* (1946) he asserts that the existence of ethical qualities is no reason for belief in God.   His argument is as follows.   If evolution is to take place, he says, it is essential that clans should exist in isolation so that they may " nurse " their own genes without dilution, and this can only happen if individual members are kind to one another, but cruel and vindictive to their enemies. There is, therefore, a *need* for both love and hate.   Therefore both love and hate just came into existence and evolution explains their presence quite easily without anything of a miraculous nature.   Exactly the same idea is to be found, repeated again and again, in the writings of Julian Huxley. Thus, in his *Evolutionary Ethics* (1943), he assures us that evolution " transforms the world stuff . . . it is creative." Again, in *Religion without Revelation* (1927), he states that if X-rays or strong electric currents were abundant in nature, sense organs would be evolved to detect them.   On this view it might be supposed that, after a long time, countries with good motor roads, ought to evolve animals with wheels instead of legs.

The assumption that things will just turn up because they are wanted is about as sensible as saying that the toy motor car which the child receives in its Christmas stocking does not have to be made in a factory at all, for its existence is

[1] *Nature*, 1873, 7, p. 417.
[2] *Darwinism and its Critics*, 1935.

quite easily explained by the fact that it is wanted by the child. This is the level at which materialists and agnostics generally argue when they want to make the public believe that evolution removes a need for belief in God.

*   *   *   *   *

After making these preliminary remarks we may now pass on to consider briefly the mechanism of evolution. In what way might evolution have taken place—if, indeed, it did take place?

The more reputable evolutionary writers, for the most part, tell us that Darwin's theory of evolution by natural selection is still by far the most plausible mechanism for evolution that has yet been suggested. We shall, therefore, start by considering natural selection in the light of modern biological knowledge. After that we may mention one or two other possible theories of evolution.

Darwin's theory involves two important points. First of all it assumes that the individuals within a species vary slightly from one another and that it is these variations which are selected by nature and form, so to speak, the raw material of evolution. (These changes must, of course, be heritable, that is to say they must be capable of being handed on to the next generation.) Secondly, Darwin assumed that if such changes were selected over long intervals of time, it would be found that the process was creative, that is to say that entirely new adaptations and structures would come into existence. We shall now examine these points in turn.

First, then, with regard to the changes. In practice we always find, even within a pure in-bred population, that individuals vary slightly from one another. Darwin believed that natural selection operated upon these variations but we now know that he was wrong, for such variations cannot be handed on from one generation to the next. Thus, in Mendel's experiments, the individuals of a race of pure bred tall peas, varied slightly in height, but the progeny of the tall ones was not on an average taller than the progeny of the short ones.   Another cause of variation is to be found in Mendelian factors alone and is due to the fact that the group of individuals is not sufficiently inbred. But once again, it has been found that this offers no evolutionary possibilities.   By selection, a particular character can be chosen and made to appear in all the individuals, but after that nothing further can be done.   It is this kind of selection which has been used in the production of domestic animals and of wheats which will withstand cold, hot, dry or moist climates.   There are no evolutionary possibilities here.

It is now generally recognized that one and only one possibility remains—the possibility that evolution is the result of *mutations* or changes both in the ultimate units of heredity, the genes, and in their relative arrangements.

In its earlier days, genetics seemed to provide a definite refutation of Darwin's ideas.   For Darwin assumed that there would be innumerable very small heritable differences between each generation and the one that preceded it, while the newer science indicated that heritable variations were not small at all, but always involved large sudden changes.   For this reason alone, many writers argued that evolution, as Darwin had pictured it, was quite out of the question.

At the present time it is no longer felt that this constitutes a difficulty.   In the early days very large mutations were chiefly studied, simply because they were large and so were the first to attract attention.   But it is now known that large mutations are not the most common variety— very small mutations occur much more frequently.   In nature sudden large mutations seem to have been important in the production of new varieties of plants, especially those isolated in small colonies, as on a mountain-side, but apart from this they are probably unimportant.   In fact, it is generally found that, when large mutations occur, it is exceedingly difficult to keep the new individuals alive even under laboratory conditions—in nature they would almost certainly die at once.   Darwin was right, therefore, in supposing that innumerable very small heritable variations do occur in nature—though they occur much less frequently than he supposed.

In mutations, therefore, we have the only kind of heritable variation known to science upon which natural selection might work in order to produce new varieties and species. Yet, although many thousands of mutations have now been studied, not a single clear instance has been found in which a mutation has made an animal more complicated, brought any new structure into existence or even effected any new adaptation of a radical nature.

We know very little about how genes are constructed or how they reproduce—though plausible suggestions on both points have been made.   But, whatever genes may be like, they are certainly very wonderful structures, containing a hundred thousand atoms and upwards, practically every one of these in exactly its right position.   If we could see them magnified to visible dimensions we should almost certainly mistake them at once for wonderfully complicated machines.   It is evident that these " machines " are so elaborately built that, not only can they perform the quite remarkable feat of reproducing themselves, but they must also perform their proper function.   That is to say, as an animal develops, the genes must bring about amazingly complicated chemical reactions which ensure that its organs develop properly, and in their right order.   Moreover, the genes have to work in harmony with one another —even alterations in their relative positions are generally harmful and often fatal.   The " machines " must, in fact, be far more complicated and carefully designed than anything mankind has yet been able to make in factories.

On the other hand, as Ubbelohde[1] has pointed out, the modern development of automatic machines which can perform elaborate calculations, or react to objects at a distance (as in radar) does help us to understand that matter may be capable of being organized in such a way as to perform these wonders.

When we think of genes in this light, we at once see a reason for the fact that mutations are either harmful or else neither harmful nor beneficial to a species—though, occasionally, they may enable it to adjust itself to its surroundings. For, if we take a carefully designed and delicate machine like a watch, and throw things at it, we shall certainly effect changes in its structure. But although, in imagination, these changes *might* on very rare occasions prove useful, they will never be changes of a constructive kind. To take an admittedly ludicrous example, we may imagine a watch from one side of which protrudes a knob which makes it decidedly difficult for the old gentleman who owns the watch to slide it into his pocket. But, after bombarding the watch with steel pellets, it might happen that the knob would be knocked off, to the great delight of the owner. This we *can* imagine, but no one would suppose that, if we bombarded the watch long enough, the steel pellets would create a new mechanism capable of striking the hours.

Turning again to biology, it is easy to imagine that, occasionally, mutations might help individuals to adapt themselves to their surroundings, after which the mutants may replace their fellows as a result of natural selection. But to go further and to imagine that a series of such changes, however long continued, would in the end create new and highly complex mechanisms, so making organisms more complex than they were before, would seem to be highly ridiculous. The plain fact is that if the picture presented to us by modern geneticists is anything like true,

[1] A. R. Ubbelohde, *Time and Thermodynamics*, 1947, p. 94 ff.

evolution as a result of the natural selection of favourable mutations would seem to be a thousand times more difficult to accept to-day than it has ever been. Indeed, so far at any rate as the writer has been able to discover, only one attempt has ever been made to show how evolution could have occurred as a result of mutations. This was in the early days and the argument was so full of pitfalls and false assumptions that, even its author (H. J. Muller) seems now to have dropped it like a hot cake![1]

Thus, despite the vast amount of work that has been done on genetics in recent years, it now seems clear that no light whatever has yet been thrown upon the fundamental problems of evolution—a fact of which authorities are on the whole well aware. Thus, in reviewing an important work on genetics and evolution, a writer in *Nature* remarks : " The fundamental causes of evolution on the grand scale, as it has occurred through geological

---

[1] H. J. Muller, *Scientific Monthly*, 1929, **29**, 481. (The writer is indebted to Dr. Julian S. Huxley for drawing his attention to this memoir.) Muller makes no mention of the subject in his comprehensive Terry Lectures (*Science and Criticism*, 1943). In the earlier memoir he estimated that natural selection, taken over geological time, might be capable of picking the fittest individuals out of a number which could not greatly exceed $10^{4 \times 10^6}$ potential individuals. By making simplifying assumptions he also calculated that selection of this degree of effectiveness might be capable of creating the degree of organization at present found in animals. His assumptions, however, really amount to assuming what he wanted to prove. Thus, (1) he assumes that natural selection functions at every stage in evolution. (See later, p. 138). (2) He assumes that genes might be built up to their present order of complexity as a result of very few, about twenty, successful random mutations. But the synthesis of even simple molecules (vitamins, glucose, etc.) involves about this number of stages. (There are probably about twenty to twenty-five stages in the synthesis of glucose in the plant.) If we suppose that each mutation corresponds to a new synthetic stage on the way towards building the final molecular structure of a gene, it is likely that thousands, perhaps even hundreds of thousands, of mutations would be necessary, and this alone would destroy Muller's argument. (3) Very long periods of time are allowed in the calculations, yet phyla appear suddenly in the rocks (see later, p. 173). Muller's attempt only shows how glaringly impossible it is to suppose that the world of living nature could have been built up by a natural selection mechanism.

time and in the fashioning of the great groups of animals
and plants, cannot yet be described or explained."[1]

* * * * *

The difficulties, then, in the way of the mutation theory
of evolution are very great. But let us suppose that, in
theory, they can be successfully overcome—should we
now be able to accept the evolutionary picture?

To answer this question, we must appeal to the actual
facts of nature. Do the facts of biology suggest that
natural selection has been responsible for the creation
of species?

In the first place the doctrine of natural selection requires
that the various organs, instincts and adaptations of organisms should be of a type that confers a distinct advantage
upon a species—for, otherwise, they could not, normally,
have been selected.

Now one of the most striking results of scientific enquiry
over the past few decades has been to show that organisms
frequently possess powers which are either never brought
into use at all, or only very rarely called upon for service.
An illustration of this is found in embryology. As an
embryo is growing, elaborate mechanisms are called into
play as the different parts develop. In rare instances it may
happen that one of these mechanisms goes wrong, but it
is then found that a totally new mechanism may take over
and produce the required structure. The number of these
" double assurance " mechanisms is considerable and there
may even be more than two—perhaps three or four—
mechanisms for bringing about the same result, these only
being called upon to function when the mechanism above
them on the list fails. As such failures are exceedingly
rare, it is difficult to understand how entirely new mechanisms could have been evolved to function in their place
when they happen to fail.

[1] I. Manton, *Nature*, 1946, **157**, p. 713, in a review of M. J. D.
White's *Animal Cytology and Evolution*, C.U.P., 1945.

Animal psychology has revealed further points of the same kind. Dogs can detect differences in tone much better, even, than most human beings, but it is considered doubtful whether they make any use of this ability in nature. The same point is even more strikingly illustrated by the performance of many animals under laboratory tests which have no known counterpart in nature. Speaking of the performance of birds and dogs in orientational tests, Katz remarks : " We are more and more compelled to the view that nature has equipped creatures far more lavishly than necessity requires."[1]

Lower animals and even insects also possess powers of dealing with situations which hardly suggest natural selection. E. S. Russell has discussed a number of instances of this kind[2]. Thus the caddis larva *Molanna* when about to pupate, buries itself in the sand, out of which it constructs a case around its own body. In experiments in which a large amount of the case was cut away from behind, no two out of fifty-four larvæ reacted in precisely the same way, but all brought the case into a usable condition once more. When the larvæ were turned out of their own cases and put into the cases of larger or smaller larvæ, they were again able to deal with the new problems encountered. In all such instances, as Russell points out, the larvæ had to deal with novel situations, unknown before either to themselves or to their ancestors, so that their effective responses cannot possibly be accounted for by natural selection.

All this falls into line with many elementary facts that have been known for a very long time. The survival value of two kidneys can scarcely be appreciably greater than that of one. The same is true of the lungs, eyes and so on. It might be urged that there is a small survival value in such cases, for if one organ is diseased, there is

[1] D. Katz, *Animals and Men*, 1937, p. 62.
[2] E. S. Russell, *The Directiveness of Organic Activities*, 1945, pp. 18 ff.

still the other to go on with. But while a very few individuals may benefit enormously, it is difficult to believe
that such factors are of much importance to the race.
Indeed, if natural selection operates in instances of this
kind, it is difficult to understand why *all* organs do not
increase in number. Why is it, for instance, that we have
not evolved an extra heart in case the first one fails, and
why not a third eye in case the first two are destroyed ?
It would seem clear that natural selection is unlikely
ever to be in a position to give an answer to these
questions without a great deal of unsatisfactory special
pleading.

In this connexion it is interesting to note that modern
science has undermined the criticism of Hume : " It is
vain . . . to insist upon the uses of the parts in animals or
vegetables and their curious adjustments to each other.
I would fain know how an animal could subsist, unless its
parts were so adjusted." We now know that the older
naturalists were right when they insisted that teleology cannot fairly be dismissed in this off-handed way. Although
a certain amount of adjustment is necessary for an animal
to exist at all, there is a great deal more present than is
strictly necessary.

The difficulty we have mentioned is by no means
imaginary or unimportant.   Bruce Bliven, an American
journalist, who had interviews with hundreds of American
scientists some years ago, records the fact that this point
was frequently mentioned as one of the greatest of all the
unsolved mysteries of science.[1] All the scientists were
agreed that natural selection would account for very
simple instances of adaptation. If a group of rabbits,
some black and some white, were to be let loose in a
country where the ground was largely covered with ice
and snow, the black ones would die out first because their
enemies would find them more easily.   After a few genera-

[1] Bruce Bliven, *Men Who Make the Future*, Eng. Ed., 1943, p. 152.

tions, therefore, all the rabbits would be white. Everyone agreed that natural selection could explain simple adaptations of this kind, but it was widely felt that it could do no more.

As a further example of the innumerable instances of adaptation which natural selection does not explain, we may cite the case of termites, which can digest wood with the aid of the protozoa which live in their stomachs. It is hard to believe that the insects suffered a mutation which made them want to eat wood that was indigestible to them, that at precisely the same time their bodies became adjusted to enable them to maintain colonies of protozoa, and that at precisely the same time also, mutations took place in the local colonies of protozoa which enabled them to live in the stomachs of the termites—after which both termites and protozoa lived happily ever after! Again, what of the metamorphoses in the life cycles of insects and amphibia? Natural selection might, conceivably, explain why tadpoles learn to swim, feed and run away from their enemies more efficiently than did their remote ancestors (assuming this to be a fact), but does it throw any light on why they turn into frogs?

Then there is another difficulty. As we have already observed, practically all believers in natural selection today are agreed that mutations in the direction of evolutionary advance do not take place suddenly. Like Darwin, they hold that evolution could only have come about as a result of a very large number of small changes. Mathematical biologists (Haldane, Wright, Fisher) have been concerned to show that even if the changes were very small indeed, so small that they only confer a very small advantage upon a species, the mutant forms would in the end be able, under certain circumstances, to oust the older forms—provided sufficient time be allowed.

Now if this be so it becomes more than ever clear that the types of structure which have been evolved can only be those which would benefit the individuals which possess them at *every* stage of development. For natural selection cannot operate at all unless every stage in the gradual process of evolution is one which confers enough advantage for the animal to oust its predecessors.

Now this is exactly what we do not find in nature. The eye is no use at all to an individual unless it is all there. Its very usefulness depends upon the fact that it consists of a number of parts which are neatly and wonderfully adjusted to one another. It is very difficult to understand how, if we simply start with a light-sensitive patch of skin, and allow natural selection to work upon repeated mutations, anything like an eye will eventually be formed. Even the embryonic development of the eye, as of other organs, is against such a theory. For the eye in the embryo does not slowly become more complicated, but the parts of it seem rather to be made separately and then to be fitted together to form the eye at a later stage in development.

Again, the electric organs of fishes are entirely useless unless they are able to produce a shock sufficiently great to destroy or paralyse the smaller fishes or animals upon which the species possessing them happens to feed. Why, then, were they not removed in the early stages of evolution, long before they had developed to the point of usefulness ? Darwin himself felt this difficulty, but, despite the lapse of nearly a century, it is no less formidable to-day.

Modern research in biochemistry has revealed numerous other difficulties of a similar kind. Elaborate biochemical syntheses are often used by living matter which enable it to build up some chemical substance which it requires for life out of simpler materials. Now syntheses of this kind cannot be performed in a single stage. They may and often do require half a dozen or more stages, and each one of these occurs only in the presence of a complicated and very specific substance called an *enzyme*. Yet it has been found that the intermediate substances that are formed may be of no value whatever and may, in fact, not be of the slightest use in any kind of known living organism. So once again the same difficulty arises. When the whole elaborate machine is running it is valuable to the organism, but taken separately its parts are of no use at all. Yet it seems hardly likely that the whole arrangement could have come into existence by chance all at once.

This fundamental difficulty has never been faced. In fact some biologists, in their attempts to present natural selection as a plausible hypothesis, often seem to ignore it quite deliberately, especially when the development of some special structure is being considered. Take, for example, the origin of the feathers of birds. Some years ago Pycraft suggested that birds were derived from creatures with scales. He suggested that first of all the scales on the arms " frayed out " adaptively and that after this the same process continued over the rest of the body. On this suggestion another biologist comments as follows : " This theory was somewhat uncritically copied by one writer after another, mostly without any attempt to explain how the transformation of a scale into so strikingly different a structure as a feather might be supposed to have occurred, or to meet the obvious difficulty that frayed out scales would have been useless as supports without the complex inter-locking mechanism which distinguishes the feather and which can hardly have been developed all at once."[1] Put in other words, the fundamental fact that feathers in their early stages would have conferred no advantage at all upon semi-birdlike creatures, has been slurred over. Perhaps the point need not be further laboured.

On the side of theory, the doctrine that natural selection

[1] B. W. Tucker, in *Evolution. Essays . . . presented to E. S. Goodrich.* Ed. G. R. de Beer, p. 330. Tucker himself proposes that the object of the feathers in the first case was to keep birds warm, but his theory does not explain how they became adapted for flying.

is the cause of evolution runs contrary to the whole conception of genes which has been built up as a result of
modern work in genetics. Direct observation of nature
also shows convincingly that natural selection cannot have
been the main cause of evolution for, while it enables us
to explain lesser things, it leaves the fundamental issues
untouched. Indeed, no matter from what angle we look
at the matter, the difficulties in supposing that evolution
could have taken place in this manner could scarcely be
more formidable than they are. Natural selection has not
yet enabled us to understand how a single complex
mechanism ever came into existence.

If natural selection is inadequate, what other possibilities
are open ? How do the other mechanisms of evolution
which have been proposed at various times fare in the
light of modern science ?

The most important of these is Lamarck's theory of
use-inheritance, or, as it is often called, the inheritance of
acquired characters. This theory was accepted by Darwin
and utilized by him whenever the theory of natural selection seemed inadequate to account for the facts.

In modern times an enormous number of experiments
have been performed with a view to confirming the theory
of use-inheritance. In the early days, especially, many
claims were made. Nevertheless, more careful experiments have shown in nearly every instance that the results
cannot be confirmed, or that they are more easily explained
in other ways.

The subject is full of pitfalls for the unwary. If all the
individuals being tested do not possess identical genes,
it is almost impossible to avoid some unfair selection in
the breeding of the next generation. Often, therefore, it
will seem as if use-inheritance has been confirmed when
this is not really so. This is the explanation of McDougall's
famous experiments on rats, as a result of which he claimed

that the acquired ability of rats to find their way through his mazes was inherited by the next generation.[1]

Suffice it to say that, so far as the form or structure of animals is concerned, there is not a single claim to have established the theory of use-inheritance which has not now been discredited. But even if, at this late date, one or two genuine instances of use-inheritance were to be discovered, they would still be of such an exceptional character, that it would be difficult to suppose that such inheritance was a serious factor in evolution.

Despite the total failure of all experiments, a very plausible case can be made out for use-inheritance and there are one or two well-known biologists who take it seriously. Thus, H. F. Osborn, speaking as a paleontologist, believes that the evidence for use-inheritance is overwhelming. He holds that, whatever may or may not happen as the result of experiments done in the laboratory, the fossil evidence can only be interpreted in this way. Wood Jones adopts a similar attitude. Among other biologists very few have been convinced.

The main difficulty with regard to use-inheritance is not that plausible fossil evidence is lacking, or even that laboratory experiments have not confirmed it (though the last objection is very serious). The difficulty is felt, rather, to be physical. No one has ever suggested a conceivable means by which, shall we say, a leg muscle which has

---

[1] See F. A. E. Crew. *Jour. of Genetics*, 1936, **33**, p. 61. There are a very few recent cases which have not yet been explained away, such as the alleged ability of stick insects to inherit an acquired liking for ivy, and the inheritance of an acquired liability to cancer in rats. It is, however, generally felt that such cases can be explained without accepting the theory of use-inheritance in the proper sense of the term. It is not unlikely that in rare cases a chemical substance introduced into an animal as a result of a disease or change in diet, and accompanied perhaps by the loss of another chemical substance, will affect the reproductive cells in a permanent way. The genes, in dividing, will have to get on as best they can in new chemical surroundings, and so, in reproducing, their structure may be slightly altered. Such instances are, however, exceedingly rare and, while they may enable an organism to adapt itself to new surroundings, the amount of adaptation possible seems to be very limited.

become enlarged and strengthened through physical exercise, could so modify the genes of the body, that the alterations would be handed on to a man's offspring.

This total inability to suggest any possible way in which use-inheritance could take place, has caused most scientific workers to regard it as a kind of superstition.   The doctrine really involves a belief that, when our bodies have been altered in some way, they bring about a totally different kind of event—they alter the chemical structure of the genes, not at random, but in such a way that when these genes have developed, they produce alterations in the next generation similar to the alteration that took place in the body of the parent.   In the absence of overwhelming proof this is extremely difficult to believe.   In many ways it is closely comparable to a belief in astrology, for it seems as fantastic to hold that large scale changes in our anatomy effect corresponding changes in the exceedingly minute genes inside our cells, as it does to suppose that movements of the planets bring about corresponding changes in men— the relative proportional sizes in the two instances being, perhaps, about the same.   Or again, we may compare use-inheritance with the widespread view that when a pregnant woman has seen a curious object, her child will be correspondingly marked or deformed.   Excellent anecdotal evidence of this widely held belief can be produced, but the physical difficulty involved—the idea that a sight of an object can somehow mark a baby—is enough to make practically all scientists and doctors regard the belief as a superstition.   In exactly the same way the physical difficulty involved in use-inheritance is felt to be so formidable that few scientifically-minded biologists are disposed to take it seriously.

Before leaving this subject, a few words may be said about the history and influence of use-inheritance.   Until well into the present century, the doctrine was almost universally accepted as a fact and it exercised considerable influence outside biology.   Books by the older generation of

theologians abound with statements of the following kind :
" Man is a bundle of inherited tendencies, and will, in turn
transmit his nature, with its new marks of good and evil,
to those who come after him." [1]   Freud, too, accepted the
idea when he claimed that man has a racial memory of sex.
Jung's psychology, with its system of archetypes, seems to
be quite definitely pledged to the support of use-inheritance.
The effect of the doctrine of use-inheritance upon morals
was also considerable.   Many of the older books insist,
with the utmost conviction and gravity, that sexual mal-
practices cause lack of health to later generations.

The modern world has accepted the disproof of use-
inheritance with a good deal of ill-considered enthusiasm.
As Sir W. Langdon Brown has put it : " Loud voices
proclaim that it matters not if we live good lives or bad
for, apart from direct disease or social degradation, we
cannot hand on to our descendants any virtue or vice, any
talents or degeneracies that we may have acquired during
our lifetime." [2]   But, as the same writer points out, there
is undoubtedly a sense in which acquired habits *are* handed
on, even though it is not a strictly biological sense : they
are handed on by influence in the family.   In this way the
next generation is influenced much more rapidly and much
more effectively, even, than if the biological doctrine of use-
inheritance were true.

Several other more or less vague views have been suggested as to the causes of evolution, but none of them is
worth considering in detail as they find little support to-day.
Thus, Samuel Butler tried to explain evolution by supposing
that as each generation managed to solve its problems by
cunning rather than luck, a racial memory guaranteed that
the powers were not lost to subsequent generations.   He
summarized the antithesis between his own and Darwin's
theory by the title of one of his books, *Luck or Cunning?*
Not only is his view faced with the difficulty that use-

[1] James Orr, *The Christian View of God and the World*, 1893, p. 189.
[2] *Nature*, 1943, **152**, 467.

inheritance cannot be proved but it also seems clear that such facts as those adduced by Russell in connexion with caddis larvæ are sufficient to discredit it.

According to another view· (orthogenesis) species are made in such a way that they cannot help evolving along certain predetermined lines. Thus Bateson, for example, is reported to have said that " evolution is an unfolding of potentialities in the germ plasm of the originals of living things." Obviously this view will not cover more than a very limited number of facts, but it might be used to explain why, for example, quite a number of groups of animals in the remote past went on increasing in size, and developed horns, or, again, why ancient shell fish became progressively more coiled. It might be applied, also, to ants and termites which, though they had (as is supposed), very different evolutionary origins, developed similar social habits.

If carried to its logical limits, this view would presuppose that, in the first germ of life that appeared on earth, all subsequent creatures were enveloped. Far, therefore from helping to explain the origin of species in a scientific way, it simply means that God performed one prodigious miracle at the beginning instead of a number of later and much smaller ones. It also has the disadvantage that we have to believe that the simpler forms of life were really the more complicated ones, because they held the later more complicated ones concealed within themselves. To hold such a view is surely to give up ever trying to make sense of biology.

However, orthogenesis is probably not wholly false. Genetics has shown us that certain characters may remain recessive—that is to say that the insect which is born without wings still retains the power to produce wings in its progeny provided a suitable mutation occurs or it finds a suitable mate. Outward and visible form does not, in fact, represent the entire organization of an animal organism. Now what has been discovered in the laboratory as a result of experiments in breeding, must, without doubt, have applied also in the case of early forms of life which are known only to us through their fossils. And the facts certainly do suggest that many characters—social habits, electric organs (which have arisen independently, now from one organ, now from another) and so on—may have been recessive in the animals long before they evolved into something visible. Moreover, it appears likely that animals at the present day still retain many recessive characters which have not been realized, except very occasionally. A very few people, for instance, have the power to produce sweat which is brilliantly luminous. This suggests that, if ever occasion demanded it, a race of men *could* become luminous and so able to see in the dark. Yet, were this to happen, it would not be as a result of the " creative " power of evolution, but simply because some at least of all men at all times have possessed the mechanism for making a luminous material, for the production of which there has hitherto been no necessity.

There are no other scientific explanations of the origin of living organisms, except, perhaps, one or two of a purely verbal nature. Thus, Berg's *nomogenesis*—or *evolution by law*—does not attempt to explain how the law arises or how evolution took place.

Thus every theory of evolution has failed in the light of modern discovery and, not merely failed, but failed so dismally that it seems almost impossible to go on believing in evolution ! At this we shall doubtless be tempted to say : Never mind the mechanism, the *positive* evidence for evolution, evidence which Darwin brought forward so convincingly, is in no way discredited even if no one has yet discovered just *how* evolution works.

Before turning to consider the positive arguments for evolution, we shall first of all seek to find out whether the difficulties that we have been discussing are really fundamental or whether they are of the type that may safely be left for subsequent research to solve.

CHAPTER VIII

EVOLUTION AND PHYSICS [1]

EVOLUTION, AS WE HAVE REPEATEDLY SEEN, CAME TO BE accepted in the first place, not because it had been proved, but because it was plausible and because it was felt to fit in well with the science of the day.

In time, however, it was slowly realized that the nine-teenth-century scientific picture of the universe was by no means complete. To begin with, astronomy itself could not be explained entirely in terms of mechanics. It had long been known that hot and cold bodies could not exist simultaneously in a universe without eventually reaching the same temperature. As this uniform state had not yet been reached, it followed that the universe could not have existed eternally, but must have been created in time. In his letters to Bentley, Newton used this as an argument for a belief in God who had created the universe in the first place. This argument was wholly forgotten by a later generation of enthusiastic scientific-philosophers who imagined that a " fire-mist " had automatically condensed to give nebulæ, suns and worlds. Herbert Spencer, as we have seen, was so anxious to believe this wholly materialistic picture of the universe that he placed himself in strong opposition to established principles of physics.

In time, the rise of modern industry, with its constant demand for energy, again focused attention on Newton's argument. It became a matter of some importance to know how the various forms of energy might be converted

[1] Based in part (with the permission of the Council of the Victoria Institute) upon the author's paper, *Evolution and Entropy*, Trans. Victoria Institute, 1943, **75**, 49. Further details and references will be found in this paper.

into one another. Experience showed that mechanical work could easily be converted, without loss, into heat, but only a certain proportion of this heat could be converted back into mechanical work. Was this due to inefficient machinery, or did nature itself set the limit?

Investigation showed that the limit was set by nature. It was impossible to convert all the energy of burning coal into mechanical work by means of any engine of any conceivable kind, no matter how well the engine was constructed. In a steam engine, the proportion which could be converted depended only upon the difference in temperature between the steam and the surrounding air and, if this difference was reduced to zero, no work could be obtained. It followed that mechanical work only became available when hot bodies were heating cold ones, so that the heat energy contained in a large mass of uniform material, such as the sea, could never be used as a source of power.

Thus, the physicist and engineer came to realize that it was not enough to ask how much *energy* was contained in a lump of coal, in the steam of a boiler or in a tank of hot water; it was *also* important to know how much of this energy was available for doing work. Some measure of the availability of the energy was, therefore, required.

It was in this way that the idea of what came to be called *entropy* arose. Entropy is, in the first place, a mathematical expression only. Actually it measures not the availability but the *non-availability* of energy. Thus, in a mass of water at a uniform temperature, entropy is at its maximum and no energy is available. On the other hand, the entropy of a very hot body in cold surroundings is small and so a large proportion of the energy is available for doing work.

Every process in which heat passes from one body to another involves a rise in entropy—for a fall in entropy would mean that a cold object was heating a hot one, which is contrary to experience. But entropy need not necessarily be attached to the energy which is contained in hot or cold physical bodies, for the entropy of other kinds of energy, such as that of electricity and radiation, can also be measured.

To-day, as a result of these discoveries, Newton's argument is usually put in a more general form. It is said that, since entropy increases in every physical process—a statement often also referred to as the *second law of thermodynamics*—the entropy of the whole universe must be rising also. Now entropy can never have been infinitely small, nor can it have increased infinitely slowly (since its rate of increase falls off as it rises), so it follows that the universe could not have existed from all eternity backwards but, as Jeans has put it, must have had a creation in time. All of which is a more involved (and also more fool-proof) way of saying what Newton said a long time ago in much simpler language.

Thus far, in this chapter, we have been concerned with physics only, and have not even mentioned biology. But before we do so, there is more to learn from entropy. Why does the curious generalization about increasing entropy hold without an exception throughout the physical world ? Upon what does it ultimately rest ?

This question was answered by Boltzmann. The law rests upon one of our most fundamental ideas about the outside world, an idea without which we cannot even begin to interpret nature or to commence the study of science.

It is not easy to put the idea in words. Simplified definitions have a way of failing to allow for scores of real or apparent exceptions, and making us doubt from the start the existence of the thing we define, while on the other hand, long involved statements suggest a complexity which we are apt to suppose resides in the things we describe, instead of in the words we use to describe them. So let us resolve the difficulty by reminding ourselves of a familiar story. In the book of Genesis (43 : 33) we read of a lord of Egypt who entertained eleven men who were brothers. The men, so the story goes, " marvelled one with another " when they found themselves seated at table in the exact order of their ages.

Let us seek to face the question : why was it that they marvelled ? For answer we can only say that such an event seemed to contradict one of the basic ideas entailed in " common sense." The men had never heard of the laws of probability, of entropy, or of the second law of thermodynamics, but they rightly suspected that the long arm of coincidence would hardly have arranged them in just that way. Somehow, they guessed that intelligence was at work, though to all appearances this could hardly have been the case. In the end, so it would seem, they decided to trust to appearances instead of intuition. Nevertheless, they soon learned that their intuition had not deceived them.

The idea, in short, is simply this. Order does not arise of its own accord ; it does not come out of nothing, and we must not explain it away by chance. On the other hand order is easily lost spontaneously. Having now put the idea in words, we must not let our minds be side-tracked by purely verbal questions—by discussing precisely what we mean by " order," by " increase " in order or by " chance." These question are legitimate enough in their place but, even should we fail to answer them, our fundamental idea or law will not be any less true because we cannot find the words with which to express it.

Now Boltzmann showed that the law of entropy is only a particular instance of the much wider law which we have already mentioned. He showed that what was really taking place when a hot object warms a cold one, is the general disordering of the molecules. Using this simple conception, he was also able to show how the entropy of a system can often be calculated.

At this point it will make our discussion easier if we can

agree on a name for the law that disorder tends to increase, the basic law of which the law of entropy is only one particular illustration. Several suggestions have been made. Some writers now use the word " entropy " in a much wider sense than it possesses in physics : they use it simply to mean " disorder." In this sense " the law of entropy " must be understood to mean that disorder increases but cannot arise spontaneously from chaos. This use of the word is, however, apt to lead to confusion, for to many people the word " entropy " is still nothing more than a name given to a mathematical formula. In 1936 the suggestion was made that the wider principle should be referred to as the *Law of Morpholysis* (*morphe* = form, *luo* = to loose), and we shall use this expression here.

Ultimately not merely physics, but all science depends upon the truth of the law of morpholysis, for science is concerned to explain, or rather explain away, the many apparent exceptions to the law. It seeks to prove that they are not really exceptions at all, but mere side-shows which result from the general loss of order throughout the universe.

There was a time when many people would have said that order did not need explaining. They were content to accept as a fact the spontaneous generation of animals from slime or, as we saw in an early chapter of this book, to believe in the spontaneous generation of animals during their embryonic life. Quite elaborately shaped fossils were regarded in much the same light and so did not need explaining ; there was no need to connect them with creatures which once had lived. Even implements, such as axes and hammers, which had been found in the ground, were supposed to have been produced by a natural " formatrix." Thus one writer (Adrianus Tollius, 1649) published diagrams of various implements and explained that, according to most naturalists, they were " generated in the sky by a fulgurous exhalation conglobed in a cloud by the circumfixed humour." But Tollius himself was sceptical. He thought it very strange that the axes should have holes in them, all ready for the insertion of sticks, if they had really been made in this way. In other words, he appealed directly to the law of morpholysis.

Only when it was realised that natural forces could not make order spontaneously was it possible for science to begin. Science was impossible so long as each interesting new example of order—a beautifully shaped crystal, cloud formation, striations on rocks or the form of waves on water—could be ascribed to self-ordering principles in nature.

How then, precisely, does science explain the production of order ? To answer this question, let us consider the steam engine once more. In this machine steam is allowed to expand ; some of its energy is turned into useful work while the rest goes to warm the air outside. The useful work appears, therefore, as a kind of " side-show " in the warming of a cold body by a hot one.

If we think about the matter more closely we shall see that a very wonderful thing is happening. In the hot steam the molecules of water are darting ceaselessly and rapidly in every direction yet, out of this medley, the steam engine gets useful work—the *ordered* movement of a piston along a cylinder against an opposing force. It is as wonderful as if millions of fire-flies, flitting aimlessly in any and every direction, should suddenly produce a stream of tiny points of light moving in the same direction and exactly parallel to one another. Surely the engine creates order where there was none before ! But how is the miracle performed ?

The physicist has found a simple and adequate answer. He has discovered that, despite appearances, the miracle is *not* performed at all. Molecules which happen to be moving towards the piston are alone able to give up their energy—the rest just rebound repeatedly from the cylinder walls until they, too, chance to be moving in the right direction. If the process stops before the whole of the energy of the molecules has been given up—before the absolute zero of temperature is reached—only a part of the energy of the moving molecules can be converted into useful work. So the engine does not create order where there was none before. All it does is to pick out a particular kind of order (movement of molecules in a certain direction) just as a sieve might pick out grains of sand of a particular size, or a grating might pick out match-sticks which happened to lie in a certain direction.

Not only has the law of morpholysis been vindicated again and again in every science, but scientific workers of to-day almost invariably assume the law in their work, though they do not always notice the fact. For instance, if a group of meteorites were seen to fall upon the moon making craters in the arrangement shown :

A

*   *

*   *

*

the precise arrangement of these craters would universally be regarded by astronomers as being at random, and no one would be concerned to discover why the crater A, for instance, was not situated slightly to the left or to the right of its actual position. If, on the other hand, a group of craters arranged in a precisely similar way had previously been formed upon the earth, the lunar craters would at once be recognized as possessing order, and so explanation would become necessary. Astronomers and mathematicians, knowing instinctively that the order could not have arisen by chance, would at once try to " explain it away " by proving that, for instance, the known laws of force between small free objects moving in space are such as to necessitate the very configuration which had been observed both on the earth and on the moon. They would try, in other words, to show that the new example of order was only an inevitable " side-show " in the general running down of order throughout the universe.

In short, the business of science is to explain instances of the apparent production of order which are observed to occur in nature. It will seem, to the uninitiated, as if atoms and molecules sometimes arrange themselves and create something new ; but the scientist tries to show that however startling the apparent novelties that emerge, they were really present all the time ; they are the logical and deducible consequences of what was already in existence.

Before considering whether the law of morpholysis should be applied to biology, there is one apparent exception to the law which is so important that it cannot be overlooked at this point. What about the crystal ? If we watch a crystal growing, we see an apparently structureless liquid or vapour producing complex and beautiful patterns. How comes it that the molecules arrange themselves in this ordered manner ?

Crystallization takes place in two stages. Firstly, invisible " seeds " or " nuclei " come into existence and, secondly, these grow into larger crystals. There is no need to discuss the technicalities of the subject here. Suffice it to say that arrangements of the atoms or molecules in the crystal are determined wholly by their properties, though in rare instances the molecules can " fit " together in more than one way. In a few simple cases (the rare gases) the crystal structure has been successfully predicted as a result of observation made upon a gas, and there is little doubt that in time this achievement will be accomplished in many other instances. Thus the arrangement of the atoms or molecules in a crystal nucleus is *determined* before the crystal has come into existence. Just as the shape of a knitting needle determines the fact that knitting

needles, if shaken together, will collect in long thin
bundles, so the order of the crystal is already " present "
in the liquid or vapour in the form of the properties of
the molecules. The fact that, supposing we could see
them, molecules do not " look like " the crystals to which
they give rise is, of course, irrelevant. In just the same
way the sound track on a ciné film does not " look like "
the waves of sound which we hear as music or speech ; but
all would agree that the whole organization of the resulting
sound is ultimately present in the sound track. Or, to
anticipate somewhat, chromosomes and genes do not
" look like " full-grown animals—as many of the preformationists used to suppose—but they are none the less
believed to contain the organization of biological organisms.

When once a few molecules have collected together—
enough to fit into one another so as to form a crystal
nucleus—further growth takes place easily enough. As
the crystal grows the entropy of the system always increases
and, as in the steam engine, the new order of the growing
crystal is a mere " side-show " of the running down of
order in the system.

With these brief remarks we may turn to biology in
order to decide whether the law of morpholysis applies
also in this field. At once we are confronted with the fact
that all attempts to increase our understanding of biological
principles have assumed its truth. Thus Darwin himself
took it for granted that fossils were derived from once
living forms, because he assumed that such highly ordered
shapes could not have arisen of their own accord. He
assumed, also, that if two species resembled one another
closely, they must be related, because it was unlikely that
the same order could have arisen in two cases independently.
He made the same assumption in his doctrine of " pan-
spermism " which, though it has turned out to be incorrect,
he himself regarded as his second greatest discovery, and

to which he devoted so much of his life. The law of morpholysis formed the background of his thinking, just as it did that of the physicists of his day.

Every advance in biology has, indeed, assumed the truth of this law. The idea of genes in the chromosomes only arose because biologists could not believe that the organization of an animal arises anew with every generation, but must have been present in some form in the egg or sperm. Subsequent research has vindicated this bold step. Biological mechanisms by the score—the digestion of food or the circulation of oxygen by means of the blood—have been interpreted according to the rules of physics and chemistry which, in their turn, depend upon the law of entropy. A number of biologists have themselves pointed out that the processes of growing old and dying are clear manifestations of the law of morpholysis.[1] And so instances might be multiplied.

The detailed study of evolution has again and again revealed the working of the same law. Many years ago Dollo formulated the generalization that if, during the course of evolution, an organ was reduced it never again regained its original importance, while, if it disappeared altogether, it never reappeared. Even if an organ is lost which was valuable in a previous environment, and that environment is again restored, the organ does not reappear—at best some other organ takes its place.

More recent research has shown that Dollo's law applies not only to visible bodily structures, but to scores of biochemical and physiological adaptations.[2] To cite but one striking instance: a culture of *Bacillus pyocyaneus* on one occasion lost its power to make the usual bluish-green

---

[1] L. von Bertalanffy, *Das Gefüge des Lebens*, Leipzig, 1937, p. 116. H. Pictet (*Arch. de Sc.phys. et naturel*, 1915, pp.181–200) believes that old age and death are connected with the progressive stabilization of protein molecules with the consequent production of highly stable cyclic compounds.

[2] J. Needham, *Reversibility in Evolution*, Biol. Reviews, 1938, **13**, 225.

pigment. For thirty-nine years the new strain was culti-
vated, but never recovered its original colour.

Dollo's law, in fact, has been found to hold both in
anatomy and in biochemical mechanisms over an exceedingly wide range of species, nor has any definite exception
to its operation been discovered. Its relation to the law
of morpholysis is manifest : complex structures naturally
cannot arise by chance when they have once been lost.

Again, it has been found that biochemistry is intimately
related to evolution.[1] Unstable substances with much
free energy—amines, amino-acids, glycine betaine, simple
terpenes, etc., are widely distributed in plants. Stable
substances—alkaloids, resins, etc.—on the other hand, are
very restricted in their distribution, but are formed by the
condensation of the former substances into rings. Once
formed, the latter are very stable, and are therefore no longer
able to play a part in the life of the plant which they eventually
kill—sometimes killing also the entire species. The
chemical evidence thus makes it possible to recognize in
every phylogenetic series stages of juvenility, maturity
and senility. In short, the evolutionary process always
proceeds from the highly improbable—the long chain and
unstable compounds of high free energy—to the highly
stable cyclic compounds which are ill-adapted to the life
of the species, and often even cause its death.

Once again, as the discoverer himself points out, these
facts are exactly as we should expect according to the law
of morpholysis.

Modern experiments in genetics, in which mutations have
been brought about by bombarding reproducing cells
by radiation, lead to a similar conclusion. Moreover, the
fact that these artificial mutations resemble those that take
place naturally, suggest that, among the latter also, the law
of morpholysis holds true. If this is so we should hardly
expect any new structures to arise spontaneously in nature.

[1] A. V. Blagovenschenki, *Biologia Generalis*, 1929, 5, 427.

On the basis of this and much similar evidence, some biologists have boldly identified the law of evolution with the law of entropy (or of morpholysis), though not all have realized the implications involved.

Taken at their face value, these facts seem to suggest that evolution is simply the unfolding of organizations which are already present and that, despite appearances, it cannot involve any real rise in the complexity of an organism.

As we have already seen, this conclusion has much to commend it on purely biological grounds. For, according to the view of evolution called *orthogenesis*, the various species evolve along specified directions determined in advance. In more recent times Lotka, whose *Principles of Physical Biology* is stated by Needham to be " one of the three or four greatest contributions to biological thought in the present century," simply denies that any rise occurs in organizational level during evolution. H. F. Blum [1] openly confesses that, but for the fear of giving away ground to the theologians, such conclusions would certainly have had a far greater impact upon biological thought than they have, in fact, exerted. D'Arcy Thompson [2] shows how all the classical evolutionary changes found by the paleontologists can be connected together by slowly changing the geometrical co-ordinates and, finally, concludes that the great organizational gaps in evolution are to-day unbridged and likely to remain so for ever.

Thus, the direct evidence relating to evolution is not inconsistent with the law of morpholysis and often supports it overwhelmingly. This would lead us to the conclusion that the possibilities latent in evolution are very strictly limited : that evolution can never in the strict sense be constructive or creative.

[1] H. F. Blum, *American Naturalist*, 1935, **69**, 354.
[2] D'Arcy W. Thompson, *On Growth and Form*, C.U.P., 1942, p. 1093. See later, pp. 172, 173.

Since Darwin's time, however, many biologists have disagreed with this conclusion and we must inquire on what grounds they have done so. How do they attempt to face the difficulty created by the law of morpholysis ?

By far the commonest reply is one that was used both by Darwin and Huxley and has been employed by their followers right up to the present day. To quote Darwin, a fresh egg contains neither cock nor hen yet three weeks later a chicken can be found in it. " Therefore, evolution, in the strictest sense, is actually going on in this and analogous millions and millions of instances, wherever living creatures exist."[1]   What difficulty, then, can there be in accepting evolution in its wider sense ?

Many quotations in a similar sense might be cited. Two more must suffice—one by a biologist, the other by a theologian.   " Those who feel a repugnance to the Darwinian conclusion that man is descended from a humble simian ancestry should remember the marvellous ascent in each individual lifetime " (J. Arthur Thomson).   " Evolution is so undeniably true of the individual life, it is surely perversity alone that finds an insurmountable barrier to the same acceptance of the same fact in the history of the race " (Griffith-Jones, 1899).

This well-worn argument is, however, fallacious. When once an organization exists there is no physical difficulty about its reproduction—although, of course, the machinery necessary for reproduction may have to be exceedingly complicated. Because many pieces of metal are fed into the machines of a modern factory and emerge cut, shaped and ready for the assembly shop, the miracle of their design is not lessened. The fact that articles can be reproduced

[1] *Life and Letters*, 1887, ii, 202. Compare, also, *Descent of Man*, ii, 394, etc.   The quotations that follow are from J. A. Thomson, *Darwinism and Human Life*, 3rd ed., 1916, 1946 reprint, p. 22, and E. Griffith-Jones, *The Ascent Through Christ*, 1899, p. 69.   It will be remembered (p. 69) that Huxley used the same argument in his contest with Bishop Wilberforce.

any number of times throws no light on how the prototype was designed in the first place. In the same way, the fact that plants and animals can reproduce their kind, converting amorphous matter into living organisms, throws no light whatever on how the first living plants and animals arose.

In this astonishing confusion between evolution and the growth of the embryo we see history repeating itself. Modern evolutionists are still making exactly the same mistake that the old preformationists made—the mistake that finally brought their whole theory into discredit. The preformationists—or, at least, the extremists among them—overlooked the fact that complicated organizations might reproduce themselves in perfect conformity with known laws. It was this oversight which, as we saw in an earlier chapter, led them to their ridiculous encasement theory. And evolutionists, from the time of Darwin right up to within a year or two of the publication of this book, have been repeating the same mistake times without number whenever they have wished to convince themselves and others that evolution involves no new principle. Like the preformationists of the past, they consistently forget that reproduction of an existing structure in no way sheds light on the *origin* of the structure. It is this oversight, largely, which has served to divert attention away from the fundamental difficulties involved in the evolution theory.

The comparison between embryology and evolution having failed, we may now inquire what other attempts have been made to bring evolution into line with other branches of science. So far as the writer has been able to discover, only two further attempts to meet the difficulty have been made.

In 1931 it was very tentatively suggested that rises in the evolutionary scale might be likened to the steam engine, which obtains some energy in a highly ordered state at the expense of degrading the rest. In like manner organisms, by eating and finally degrading food, obtain the new organization necessary for evolution.

A number of writers enthusiastically accepted this "explanation" and supposed that evolution and entropy were no longer at variance. One well known scientist went so far as to say that since the sun's energy was always being degraded on the earth's surface, it was able to account for organization of all kinds.

Though ingenious, the steam engine analogy will not bear examination. As we have already seen, the steam engine creates no order which was not there before ; it merely makes use of molecules which happen to be moving in a certain direction. The analogy does nothing whatsoever to show how *new* types of organization can come into existence in the first place.

The misunderstanding is due to the fact that previous writers have forgotten that the amount of entropy is not the only thing that matters. To illustrate the point in a homely way, a motor car contains more co-ordinated parts than a typewriter. If, therefore, we could calculate the entropies of the motor car and typewriter, we should no doubt find that the entropy (or disorder) of the second was the greater of the two. Applying the entropy law, therefore, we might jump to the conclusion that since entropy increases in physical changes, a motor car, sufficiently shaken up in a steel box, would turn into a typewriter ! Of course this would not happen. In order to say whether a process is physically possible it is obviously *not* enough to know that entropy will increase—it is also necessary to know something about the *kind* of organizations present at the beginning and end of the process. One kind of organization does not spontaneously turn into another.

In order that complicated biological organisms should be built up, it is necessary that the sun's heat should be degraded —but this alone is not sufficient to construct them in the first place. They cannot, in fact, be constructed except in violation of the law of morpholysis of which the entropy law is one small part.

The third analogy which has been invoked is that of the crystal. Here, at all events, it is urged that remarkable new structures can come into being of their own accord as atoms or molecules organize themselves into a crystal lattice. Some writers go further than this and assert that we may see a series of rises of organization in nature : electrons and protons produce atoms, atoms produce molecules, while molecules produce crystals, or reach a still higher level in the living organism. But, as we have had cause to remark already, the shapes of crystals are the result of the properties (particularly the shapes) of the individual molecules out of which they are constructed. With complex organizations, however, this is no longer so. The individual words or letters of a page of print do not in any sense contain their final arrangement, nor is it conceivable that the intricate complexities of living organisms or their genes can be necessary consequences of the amino-acid or carbohydrate molecules out of which they are constructed.

To suppose anything of this kind—to suppose that atoms and molecules possess a power of naturally falling into the shapes of animals and plants, complete with all the intricate structures associated with life—is to make atoms and molecules themselves almost infinitely complicated. Indeed, it is only to magnify the miracle of creation a hundredfold. But, miracle or no miracle, this can hardly be the case, for carbon compounds show no particular tendency to organize themselves into biologically important compounds in the laboratory. Indeed, the difficulties of making the materials that are found so freely in nature are simply immense ; their synthesis presents difficulties as great as, and probably greater than, the synthesis of comparable substances which are of no importance in living matter.

The analogy of the crystal may be carried one stage further. In rare instances crystal " seeds " come into existence as a result of the random motions of molecules, and when this occurs they can often grow and reproduce themselves. Is it not possible that, in the same way, genes may occasionally become more complex, and then likewise perpetuate themselves ? But, here again, the study of the crystal reveals the difficulties such an hypothesis must meet. The difficulty associated with the building of a nucleus increases enormously with small rises in the complexity of a molecule, as every laboratory worker in organic chemistry is only too well aware. The fact that some very complex organic substances, such as proteins or certain viruses, crystallize relatively easily is not to the point, for investigation has shown that in such instances the organization of the crystal by no means fully represents the complexity of the molecule, identical crystals being formed despite considerable changes in chemical constitution.

Julian Huxley attempts to avoid the difficulty by invoking natural selection. " Natural selection," he writes, " achieves its results by giving probability to combinations which would otherwise be in the highest degree improbable. This important principle clearly removes all force from the ' argument from improbability ' used by many anti-Darwinians, such as Bergson." But molecular combinations are not made more probable if, when once they have been formed, they are perpetuated by being enshrined in a species. The analogy of the crystal nucleus shows us the extreme limits of spontaneous ordering in nature, and it is an analogy which is unfavourable to the mechanistic evolutionist.

The fact is that the formation of molecular structures as highly organized as those in living matter is inconceivably improbable, and no suggestion has yet been made which will alleviate the difficulty.

The violent clash between evolution and the entropy principle began to be vaguely suspected at the end of the nineteenth century. Thus, in his essay on *Evolution and Ethics* (1894), T. H. Huxley pointed out that all man-made things lose their organization—with the passing of time bridges fall and turn to ruin ; even a garden will never stay neat and tidy of its own accord, but requires constant intelligent attention. The " general cosmic process," in fact, was one in which order produced disorder, but evolution somehow worked in the opposing direction. In this way, so he supposed, the cosmic process was opposed to itself just as when one pulls a piece of string and breaks it, our two arms are in antagonism " yet both arms derive their energy from the same original source."

To-day, we know that crude analogies about the breaking of pieces of string can do nothing to save the situation. Evolution seems hopelessly at variance with fundamental scientific principles. At this point, however, those who are determined to believe in evolution as a creative process may reply as follows. They are certain that evolution has occurred, for the highly organized mammals in existence to-day were certainly not in existence in remote geological time ; but that is no reason why they should be forced to explain *how* it happened. The " how " may safely be left to future research ; meanwhile, the facts must be accepted.

Though plausible enough, this evasion cannot stand. The theory of a rising level of organization in evolution is so directly contrary to the presuppositions of all scientific thinking that it cannot be left to future discoverers to effect a reconciliation by " filling in details." If it is true that biology forces us to accept this interpretation of evolution—and all biologists are not convinced that this is so—then, if no explanation is forthcoming, let it be admitted candidly that evolution has occurred in the face of all the laws of nature : let it be admitted that theologians are right in insisting that, if the process took place at all, it was God-guided and was, in fact, equivalent to a whole series of creative acts.

After all, the biologist has no grounds for adopting an attitude wholly dissimilar to that adopted by scientists in other fields. The mechanistic biologist is at pains to show that the laws of physics and chemistry are applicable to biology ; he has, therefore, no right to postulate a law of increasing complexity in defiance of those sciences.

Nor will it do to reply that an overwhelming mass of evidence supports the theory of evolution, for in no other science has overwhelming evidence been permitted to jeopardize the very mental processes by which we seek to understand nature.

Even in biology we have already seen how, despite a large mass of circumstantial evidence in support of the theory of use-inheritance, biologists generally reject this theory. They do so because there seems to be no conceivable way in which changes in an adult animal can be transmitted to genes in its reproductive cells. In other words, the reason why use-inheritance is rejected is ultimately because the entropy principle, or the law of morpholysis, is assumed to be true. Why, then, should evidence for evolution be treated in a wholly different way ?

There are literally scores of instances in which direct experimental observations *apparently* violate the fundamental laws of science, but the laws are not called in question. Even in modern atomic physics the basic principles of science have in general remained untouched, save that in some cases the theory of probability has undermined the immediate usefulness of the principle of causality. In practically every instance, scientific explanation has had its greatest triumphs in its ability to explain away apparent exceptions.

Thus, when a stone falls to the ground it *apparently* gains energy, but no one uses this as evidence against the law of the conservation of energy ; instead, the stone is said to have possessed the energy before in a *potential*

form.   Ciné-photographs of the sun's corona show streams
of matter constantly falling towards the sun, but no sign
that they ever rise upwards to feed the " invisible hose."
Thus, direct observation seems to support the view that
matter can arise from nothing, but the conclusion reached
by astronomers is that the matter previously rose upwards
in an *invisible* form.

When a piece of red-hot iron is allowed to cool slowly,
there is a point at which it suddenly gets hotter (*recalescence*),
but no physicist suggests that the law of entropy is violated.
Repeated accurate measurements showed that the surface
tension of mercury in a vacuum was raised by admission
of air, though it was easy to prove from the entropy law
that it ought to have been lowered.   Physical chemists do
not doubt the entropy law : they hold that the measurements were vitiated by the presence of dirt ![1]   When
radium was discovered it was found to maintain itself at
a higher temperature than the surrounding air, and it was
suggested in some quarters that an exception to the law of
entropy had at last been discovered.[2]   Rutherford saw the
falsity of such reasoning immediately, and, by assuming
the truth of the entropy law, he was able to create and
develop the science of the atom.   At one time it was urged
that since animals made energy with a greater efficiency
than that predicted by Carnot's theorem for a reversible
steam engine, the animal body violated the law of entropy.
Clear-thinking physiologists saw that the evidence only
proved that the mechanism of muscle contraction was not
that of the reversible steam engine.

In face of these and many other examples, it would be
reckless indeed to see in evolution a self-ordering principle
of nature which runs contrary to the law of morpholysis.
If, in other sciences, observable events which seem to

[1] R. S. Burdon, *Surface Tension and the Spreading of Liquids*, 1940,
chap. 3.
[2] J. Needham and W. Pagel (Ed.), *Background to Modern Science*,
1938, p. 58.

contradict this law are never taken at their face value, it is difficult indeed to see why a biological theory about non-observable events in past history should be regarded in a wholly different light.

The fact appears to be that evolution, like the theory of use-inheritance before it, has now come into head-on clash with the fundamental principles of science. Nor need we be surprised at the fact. The wonder and complexity of living organisms are hardly the kind of thing that we should expect to be produced by the operation of the ordinary laws of nature, the working of which we en- counter around us. It would be easier to believe that cold bodies should heat hot ones than that disordered matter should turn itself into a mass of co-ordinated muscles, enzyme systems, nerves, bones and so on. In thinking backwards in biology we come to the same kind of impasse that we reach in physics ; we come to a point beyond which the mind can go no farther. It is easy to avoid the difficulties by just failing to think about them. That was done in the case of astronomy, when Newton's sound reasoning was ignored and it was supposed by those who never paused to face the difficulties, that a primitive fire-mist was all that was required to make the universe. It took many years before that myth could be exploded. Yet much the same thing is still being done in the case of biology. Here, also, the origin of living organisms and their subsequent development from simple to complex— if they did so develop—cannot be reconciled with the principles of science. Just as there must have been a creation of the universe, a period when the principle of the uniformity of nature most certainly did *not* operate, so we must imagine a creation at the start of life—perhaps many such creations. Whether species were created whole or whether they were created one from another, in a number of separate acts, we cannot say for certain. But we may not and cannot avoid the central fact that these events could not have been of the kind that we witness to-day.

The story is often told of a Scottish preacher who was expounding the Bible. To his congregation he said, "And now my friends we come to a difficulty. Let us look it straight in the face – and pass on!" This is exactly the attitude of many moderns towards evolution. Whole books are written on the subject in which the real issues involved are not so much as mentioned. The situation is little short of fantastic and it seems clear that a reaction is more than due.

CHAPTER IX

CONCLUSION

IN THE COURSE OF THIS BOOK WE HAVE OUTLINED THE story of evolution. We have seen how the idea gripped thinkers in the ancient world; we have traced it briefly through the Middle Ages; we have seen how the word came to be associated with the swellings in size of the infinite series of " men within men " in which the later preformationists so fondly believed; we have seen how scientists in the early part of the nineteenth century were opposed to evolution, but became almost suddenly converted as a result of Darwin's book and the controversy at the British Association in 1860; we have examined Darwin's motives and have seen that he was seeking for a way of escape from his religious convictions; we have seen that he set an example to others to make use of science as a way of escape from theology; we have examined the effects of evolutionary teaching upon society, especially in connexion with the development of big business and modern war and, finally, we have turned to consider the doctrine afresh in the light of modern scientific knowledge, only to find that evolution is in conflict with the fundamental ideas of all scientific thinking, including the very premises upon which the evolution doctrine itself was founded. Now, in this concluding chapter, some attempt must be made to collect together the " untidy ends " of the argument, to sum the matter up and so to bring this book to a close.

First of all, the question will naturally arise as to how the abundant circumstantial evidence in favour of evolution should be regarded. Darwin certainly brought forward objective grounds for his belief which require fair consideration. How do these arguments stand to-day in the light of the more complete knowledge now available to us ?

To answer this question adequately would involve the writing of a book at least as long as Darwin's *Origin of Species*. But it may be said at once that the trends of modern research have tended very greatly to lessen the force of the classical arguments for evolution, except in so far as they relate merely to selection between varieties.

At the outset it is essential to be clear that the word *evolution* may stand for two totally different ideas. It may mean that, over long periods of time, species undergo changes without ultimately increasing in complexity. Such changes might be brought about through natural selection or in some other way and, although anatomically some structures might occasionally appear more complex in later stages of evolution, this might be because certain genes which had previously been recessive had now become dominant. In this sense of the word, evolution may undoubtedly be accepted as a fact. There are the strongest possible grounds for believing that the outward forms of living organisms have changed, often considerably, during the course of geological time. But the word is often used with the suggestion of a radically different idea—the idea that, in some mysterious way, as one generation gives birth to another, a *constructive* process takes place not merely in outward form, but *genetically*. It is supposed that new and elaborate mechanisms become added, little by little, to the wonderful molecular structures of the genes and chromosomes by means of which form is handed on from parents to offspring. It is in this second sense only that evolution is in head-on conflict with the basic principles of science, for the difficulties in such a view are of exactly the same kind as the difficulties which confront such hypotheses as use-inheritance, astrology, symbolic magic, or, for that matter, perpetual motion machines.

Bearing this distinction in mind, we shall now make a

few brief comments upon some of the classical arguments for evolution.

First of all, there is the well-known argument from recapitulation—the argument that the young, in early stages of their embryonic life, resemble the adult forms of their remote ancestors, so that the embryo " recapitulates " evolutionary history. Thus medical students used to be taught that the visceral pouches in the human fœtus were gills and proved that man had emerged from fish-life. The fact that these structures never function as gills at any stage in embryonic life was conveniently overlooked.

Taken seriously, recapitulation involves a mass of enigmas and self-contradictions. Often it is absurdly irrelevant—thus the respiratory surface develops very late in the embryo, yet without it earlier forms of life would have been impossible. Again, the size of the head relative to the whole body is enormous in embryos, but very small in their ancestors. Exceptions are, in fact, so numerous that embryological arguments can be used to prove almost anything. Biologists have argued that adult descendants often resemble embryo ancestors or even (as in ammonites) that the young contain structures which disappear in later life, but appear again in the adults of descendants—the exact reverse of recapitulation. These and many other difficulties are so formidable that recapitulation is rarely used to-day as an argument for evolution though evolutionists still claim that the facts of embryology must be interpreted against a background of evolutionary thought.

Nevertheless, the facts upon which the theory of recapitulation was founded do mean something. The resemblance is particularly striking in the very early stages. As G. W. Corner remarks : " The resemblance is overwhelming. All of them (mammals) pass through a blastocyst stage. Before that, they all come from single celled ova which differ so far as can be seen through the microscope, only in small details, about as much perhaps as two watches of different makes differ from each other."[1]   What is the reason for this resemblance ?

Modern biochemistry has given more than a hint as to the answer to this question.[2]   Invertebrates secrete their nitrogen as ammonia, fishes as urea and birds as uric acid. In embryonic life birds first of all secrete ammonia, then urea, and finally uric acid.   This *might* suggest that birds started as invertebrates, passed through a fish stage and then developed wings.   However, no one even imagines that this was the case.   The secretions simply represent chemical reactions of an increasing order of complexity. It is this which gives rise to an apparent " recapitulation " and, as Needham well points out, this is a factor which was wholly overlooked by the early evolutionists.

What applies to biochemistry must apply also, even more obviously, to anatomy.   As an animal develops, its simpler parts (like its simpler chemical mechanisms) must be formed before the more complicated ones—for we should hardly expect fine adjustments and delicate organs to come into being before the main structures to which they must ultimately become attached.   In its early stages when it is still very small, the shape of an embryo will be largely determined by physical forces which play less and less part in determining shape as size increases.   In the same way a very small quantity of water takes up the form of a spherical drop but larger quantities take the shape of the containing vessel.   It is doubtless for this reason that, during the very early stages of embryonic development, various simple forms are met with whose distribution bears no relation to the boundaries of zoological classification. To explain such similarities of form by ancestral origins is ridiculous—as ridiculous as it would be to imagine that raindrops are derived from pebbles because both are round. The connexion is real enough but it is a mathematical

---

[1] *Ourselves Unborn*, 1945.
[2] See, especially, J. Needham, *Chemical Embryology*, 1931, 1629–1647.

connexion, inherent in the nature of the universe and is not due to any direct connexion between the objects.

It is difficult to resist the conclusion that exactly the same principles may apply almost as much to the later stages in embryology, as they do to the earlier—only here the general forms involved are so complicated that detailed investigation is as yet impossible. The shape of an embryo must be connected with the shapes of the molecules out of which it is constructed. Many apparent examples of recapitulation may only be expressions of the fact that all animals are built out of the same kind of materials—carbohydrates, fats, proteins and so on.

It was these physical factors which Darwin completely overlooked when he used embryology as an argument for evolution. When discussing why it is that the young differ from the old he wrote : " There is no reason why, for instance, the wing of a bat, or the fin of a porpoise, should not have been stretched out with all their parts in proper proportion, as soon as any part became visible." D'Arcy Thompson well remarks that in these words Darwin was undermining all the facts of relative size known for hundreds of years before his time.[1]

Secondly, there is the evidence of the fossils. On the whole it is generally agreed that the more advanced and complex fossils date from later times than simpler forms. But this statement needs qualifying. Graptolites, hitherto believed to have been one of the earliest forms of living organism and to have died out in early times, have now been found side by side with advanced spore-bearing plants which are generally dated a great deal later.[2] Unfortunately much of the chronology of rocks has been based upon the fossils found in them so that the dating cannot always be used as a proof of evolutionary progression. Again, fossils come on the scene suddenly in the lower Cambrian

[1] On Growth and Form, 1942, p. 86.
[2] See Phil. Trans. Roy. Soc., 1935, 224, 421.

rocks—the thousands of feet of pre-Cambrian sedimentary rocks all over the world show not a single undisputed fossil. Representatives of all the great animal phyla, except the vertebrates, appear at the base of the fossil record.   Many forms have scarcely changed at all since those early times. Later forms, where these have changed, have often increased in size, ornamentation or outward complexity of form— ridges and ornamentation have come on shells; ammonites, once straight, have begun to coil, and so on. Such increases in complexity, though interesting, seem rather superficial. We must set them against the fact that the earliest marine creatures with eyes seem to have had as perfect seeing organs as those of to-day, or, again, to quote D'Arcy Thomson : " I for one imagine that a pterodactyl flew no less well than does an albatross, and that the old Red Sandstone fishes swam as well and as easily as the fishes of our own seas." [1]

In a number of instances fossil series have been systematically examined with a view to studying the slow changes which took place.   Examples are the ammonites, the horses which are believed to have been descended from much smaller animals with five toes, and the titanotheres of the New World which started as small pig-like creatures, became progressively larger, developed horns and finally became extinct. (In some cases, notably that of the horse, even these phylogenies have been seriously challenged).   Though widely quoted as evidence of creative evolution, such instances seem rather to show that the limits of evolution are very soon reached.   Thus the slow evolution of the horse [2] consists, for the most part, of increase in size—all the other changes being mere physical adaptations necessitated by the changed dimensions. Added to this there is, however, a very occasional and quite sudden mutation.   It was as a result of such mutations that the horses lost their toes, but little evidence, if any, of anything gained in this way has come to light.

[1] Op. cit., p. 873.
[2] See G. G. Simpson, Tempo and Mode in Evolution, 1944.

Darwin was only too well aware of the tremendous gaps in the fossil record, but paleontology not having been extensively studied in his day, he expected further work to fill the gaps.   His expectations have not been fulfilled—a fact admitted to-day by even the most ardent evolutionists. Thus Needham, after saying that the gene only explains why one animal has a green liver and another a pink one, but does not explain why either of them have livers at all, goes on to say : " Still less is it possible to offer an explanation for the paucity of missing links between the phyla of the animal kingdom, for it will hardly do now to throw all responsibility on to the imperfection of the geological record, as was the common defence in Darwin's own day." [1]

Thirdly there is the evidence afforded by the distribution of animals.   Darwin found that distinct species of lizards, flowers and so on were often found on isolated islands which had clearly not been connected with one another by land for long periods of time.   Though this evidence is convincing as far as it goes, it certainly does not go very far.   No one would wish to maintain a rigid fixity of species to-day.   There seems no reason why quite large transformations should not take place, but that is a very different thing from claiming that evolution is a creative process capable of bringing entirely new and complex bodily mechanisms into existence.

Last, and by far the most important, is the evidence afforded by comparative anatomy and vestigial organs. Thus the general arrangement of the bones in the fore-limbs of dog, man and whale are similar.   Animals are built on the same general plan, a fact realized even by the ancients who spoke of the pig as " likest to the human form divine." Not only are structures arranged in the same general way but some of the smaller structures are inexplicable unless they owe their origin to an earlier form from which the animal is descended.   Thus the horse has bones in its foot that are clearly vestigial toes, but they perform no

[1] *History is on Our Side*, 1946, p. 134.

useful function now. Again, the kiwi has a small wing hidden under a thick coating of nearly hair-like feathers. The bird cannot fly and the wing is useless, " although it is asserted that the kiwi tries its best to tuck its bill under it when it goes to sleep ! "

This last argument is not very cogent unless we first of all assume what we want to prove. For it is clear that a similarity in form might quite as well be due to the fact that one mind designed the various groups of animals as to a direct link between them. Thus, there is a general similarity in form between all petrol engines, from the earliest to the latest, but it is not due to descent.

Again, it is easy to overlook fundamental differences and to exaggerate similarities. Modern experiments in psychology (for example, those connected with the memory of nonsense rhymes, which the imagination unconsciously clothes with sense) show that this mistake is most difficult to avoid. A century ago a reviewer in *Blackwood's Magazine* (April, 1845), in commenting upon the *Vestiges of Creation*, drew attention to this point in a passage which is still well worth quoting to-day. The reviewer imagines an ingenious young man, Martinus Scriblerus, who is determined at all costs to discern connexions between things quite irrespective of whether those connexions are real or imaginary. Here is the passage : " What should have prevented him from casting a philosophic glance upon the furniture in his room ? With less ingenuity that certain physiologists, he would easily detect a marvellous unity of plan. He would have probably taken the table with its four legs and the disk they support, as his great type of joinery, and would have traced a modification of this type in all the articles around him. The chair is manifestly nothing else than the table with a development of the hinder legs commonly called the back. From the chair to the sofa the transition would be ridiculously easy ; indeed, the sofa can only be considered as a variety of the chair, produced by a high state of cultivation. In the foot-stool or ottoman, the disk of the table has become thick and pulpy while its legs have dwindled into small globular supports. This exaggeration of the upper portion at the expense of the lower, is carried a step further in the chest of drawers, where the small globular supports bear a singular disproportion to the corpulent figure they sustain. In some varieties, even these knob-like legs are wanting ; but precisely in those cases, he would observe, the knobs invariably reappear in the shape of handles, which are still a sort of paw. What is the fire-screen, he would say, but a table with the disk in a vertical position ? What the fourpost bedstead, but a reduplication of the original type, a table placed on a table, the upper one being laid open ? . . . the coal-scuttle might, perhaps, present some difficulties ; but if he might be allowed to approach it through the loo-table, he would doubtless succeed in tracing here also the unity of composition. In the loo-table, the four legs have collapsed into a central column. The coal-scuttle is only a loo-table with the edges of the disk turned up—assuming a bonnet-like shape, the result perhaps of its long domesticity. In short, we believe the only insuperable difficulty Martin would encounter would be, when, after completing his survey, he would run off to a joiner to convince him of the unity of plan on which he had been so unconsciously working."

In the past, the " misplaced manifestation of the scientific urge to unify phenomena "—to quote the words of William Ellis—harmed biology considerably. " In the latter half of the eighteenth century the main preoccupation of the leaders of biological thought was to arrange all living creatures in a single series or ladder and by this means to find a single ground plan for all organic forms. To this end the most fantastic homologies were worked out. As a result of this determination to find more unity in Nature than there is to be found, biology arrived at an impasse from which it was only delivered by Cuvier's famous type-grouping system. Cuvier's great contribution was the simple discovery that living organisms separate into a small number of *distinct* grades or types. All molluscs can be represented as modifications of a primitive generalized molluscan shell. But the molluscan type is useless as a schematization of anthropoid morphology. For this we need a radically different type."[1] Thus, although there are similarities between widely separated forms, the differences also are quite as important and to forget them is to repeat the mistakes of the past. If it is fair to argue that resemblances prove a single origin, it is equally fair to argue that differences lead to the opposite conclusion.

Modern research has, however, convincingly shown that both differences and resemblances in outward form are far less significant than was formerly held to be the case. Only a small fraction of the actual organization present in the genes may be outwardly visible—a fact sufficiently obvious when we consider that each cell in our body contains a complete set of genes, though it may only fulfil one limited function. The fundamental issue is concerned with morphology on the scale of the genes, not with the few representatives of that mass of intricate molecular machinery which may happen to manifest themselves in visible structure. If this basic fact is overlooked, muddled thinking and wrong conclusions are an inevitable outcome. Evolution, at least at the materialistic level, is a chemical problem. And it cannot be too strongly emphasized that, even if visible structure is allowed to dominate our thinking, the best attested cases of evolution do not show changes as great, say, as the outward differences that are often found between male and female of the same species which are genetically almost identical.

There is no doubt, of course, that considerable changes have taken place in geological time. In many cases these changes were probably the result of random mutations followed by survival, at times of the fittest, at others of

[1] *Philosophy*, 1941, **16**, p. 198.

the luckiest. But another factor which may turn out to be of great importance is that of change in the chemical environment. When life first came upon earth, carbon dioxide was plentiful with the result that the sea contained enormous quantities of calcium in the form of soluble calcium bicarbonate. When, later on, luxuriant vegetation spread both in the sea and over the dry land, this carbon dioxide was used up and the bicarbonate was turned into insoluble carbonate. Innumerable shellfish made good use of the precipitating material—they have left us their legacy in the form of chalk cliffs and coral atolls. The larger fishes also, in those early times, made full use of the plentiful supply of calcium carbonate out of which they built their heavy armour. This armour was adopted by all the main groups and only discarded when the fish could no longer obtain calcium in sufficient quantities. After that chitinous scales replaced the older bony armour while even backbones came to be built mostly of organic material.

These facts have always been cited as evidences of evolution, and so indeed they are. But they are not evolution in the sense of rising complexity and we can hardly doubt that if the sea were ever to re-dissolve the enormous chalk and coral deposits which were laid down at that time, the fishes would once again make good use of the calcium placed at their disposal! Indeed, laboratory experiments have shown that changes in the calcium content of sea-water will rapidly produce very great changes in the morphology of living organisms. If calcium is partly removed, sea-urchins lose their spicules and foraminifera become transparent, while if it is increased, the shells of shellfish become adorned with " striæ and ridges of secondary cell substance." [1]

[1] For examples of such experiments see *Comp. Rend Soc. Biol.*, Paris, 1889 [9], Vol. I, p. 17, and *Phil. Trans.*, 1915, **206**B, 262. It may be added that the present inorganic composition of blood bears no relation whatsoever to the composition of the early sea at any epoch in geological history. (See papers by E. J. Conway in *Proc. Roy. Irish Acad.*, 1943, etc., and *Biological Reviews*. 1945.) Yet the writers of text books repeatedly assert that the compositions are similar, which is taken to prove that men were evolved from creatures that lived in the sea !

In former epochs large changes in the chemical composition of sea-water must often have occurred in isolated areas as a result of volcanic activity. This fact alone may account for new forms of foraminifera which have come into existence along geological fault lines under the sea.

Similar factors may often have operated among land animals. In goitrous areas, where iodine is deficient, the altered secretion of the thyroid gland causes visible changes in anatomy. A number of other elements, also, are necessary in traces—fluorine, zinc, phosphorus, iron, etc. Practically nothing is yet known about the long term effects of changes in this inorganic environment—changes caused by volcanic activity, by fires, by flooding, by removal of vegetation, by changes in the level of the humus and so on—but they are likely to have been profound. Not only may they have affected mammals directly but the vitamin supplies also, through their influence upon vegetation.

One conceivable way in which such changes may have affected evolution is through their effects on differential growth rates. Recent work has shown that a number of genes are concerned with the rate of growth in animals. If some of these genes work slower than others, the general shape of an animal may be altered, although the fundamental pattern remains the same. This is strikingly seen in the case of fish. If a fish is drawn on a piece of rubber sheet and the rubber is then stretched in various ways, the resulting shapes of the fish illustrate the effects of changes in the growth rates during development. These shapes are often found to resemble, exactly, various other species of fish within the same group. Nevertheless, no amount of contortion will transform a fish belonging to one group into that of another. Within the groups transformation takes place, but there is no evidence that evolution can transform the fundamental structures.

Bacteria, perhaps, show the greatest diversity of any form of life. Unspecialized forms can adapt themselves to new chemical and physical environments with quite astonishing ease.   They can be trained to live at high or low temperatures, to feed on new and unfamiliar foodstuffs, and even to thrive in the presence of deadly poisons.   Moreover, their enormous rate of reproduction makes it possible to rear many thousands of successive generations.   Here, if any- where, it might be supposed that creative evolution, if such be possible, might be induced to take place under laboratory conditions.   Yet the evidence is wholly negative. Wonderful adaptations take place, adaptations which can be explained in terms of changed enzyme balance, yet even when a colony of bacteria seems to be farthest removed from its original form it may suddenly revert to its starting point.   Despite prolonged study, nothing even approaching evolution, in the constructive sense of the word, has ever yet emerged.   Hinshelwood, the pioneer in much of this work, summarizes his conclusions as follows : " Enzymes in linked systems may wax and wane in amount according as the supply of their intermediates varies ; division may be advanced or retarded, the modes of cleavage of nuclear material may vary.   But all these things happen without any change in the fundamental protein patterns of the basic cell constituents.   To change these would require an upheaval of a much more profound kind.   This is doubtless why variation occurs between well defined limits only : why biochemical characters may change quantitatively and great morphological differences may be produced, and yet the species . . . remains inviolate."   Hinshelwood then goes on to point out that the reason why one species cannot change into another is that such a transition would involve " almost transcendent thermodynamic improbability." [1]

Thus in the light of recent work and developments in our understanding of what evolution involves, it can no longer be claimed that the biological evidence supports

[1] C. N. Hinshelwood, *Biological Reviews*, 1944, Vol. *19*, p. 150.   See also *The Chemical Kinetics of the Bacterial Cell*, 1946.

evolution[1]; rather the contrary. Taken as a whole, the evidence goes to show that the changes which are observed, whether in the laboratory or in the fossil record, are outward only. And outwardly such processes are striking enough. Plants alter their size, the shape of their leaves or the smell of their flowers; insects may lose or gain their wings, their eyes or other parts of their anatomy. With animals it is harder to experiment, but there is little reason to doubt that here, too, great changes in form are possible and that, in the course of ages, one species may turn into another—as indeed has probably happened among horses and titanotheres. All this may be granted and yet, underneath, the fundamental protein patterns remain the same.

Thus a careful consideration of the arguments shows, quite clearly, that the evidence for evolution of the first kind is overwhelmingly strong, but that that for the second, the constructive kind, is apparently negligible. It is because these two meanings of the word have not been distinguished that evolutionary writers have repeatedly given evidence for the first and assumed that this was evidence for the second also. To take a close analogy— the word " evolution," if applied to astronomy, might be used in two senses. In the first place it would stand for *change*—for the fact that the earth was not always as we know it, but was at one time, let us say, a part of the sun, while stars might be said to have " evolved " through

[1] Instincts are sometimes cited as affording incontrovertible evidence of the evolution of increasing organization. It is said that ants, bees and termites cannot always have lived in colonies. Somehow or other their remarkable instincts must have evolved. Yet the evidence seems to suggest that instincts are remarkably constant. There are birds which still migrate over high mountain ranges, although better routes are available. It is supposed that these mountain ranges were thrown up after the instincts were formed. Bees, ants and termites have possessed their social organization unchanged right back to the earliest days and, conjecture apart, there seems to be no definite proof of a time when they existed without it. If the evolution of instincts is almost infinitely slow to-day, why should we suppose that it was once enormously rapid in early geological history ? Instinct is, in any case, a subject about which little is known and it is hardly a safe guide in making wide generalizations.

their various stages. All such " evolution " is completely reconcilable with physics, for in all present cosmic events, entropy or disorder increases. But Herbert Spencer also spoke of " evolution " in astronomy in a totally different way ; he applied it to origins and claimed that a primitive disordered gas, scattered throughout the universe, would naturally have " evolved " into the universe as we know it. " Evolution " in this sense was violently opposed to the principles of scientific thought.

In precisely the same way and for the same reason, evolution in biology may stand for one of two things and confusion must arise unless they are distinguished. In the first sense evolution is doubtless true, in the second it is very likely false or, *if true*, it involves miracles quite as startling as any demanded by the special creationist.

It is interesting to consider the situation which has arisen to-day in its historical perspective. As science has progressed the idea that blind nature possesses a self-ordering power has been vanquished in one domain after another until, to-day, evolution is probably the only widely accepted doctrine which violates the law of morpholysis. Yet, in the nineteenth century, evolution replaced special creation, believers in which were fundamentally right in saying that natural forces could not bring complex organisms into existence. With this, the history of embryology, outlined in an earlier chapter, provides a close historical parallel. Preformationism, which dominated the scientific world from 1680 to 1780, was a great hindrance to biological study, and the latter benefited greatly when epigenesis came to be generally accepted. The preformationists, like the special creationists, made foolish mistakes, but these mistakes were not an essential part of their theory which insisted, fundamentally, upon the fact that the organization of animals must be represented inside their eggs. Epigenesis, on the other hand, amounted to spontaneous generation in

eggs and was fundamentally unscientific, though this fact
was not realized at the time. Ultimately, however, genetics
proved that the preformationists were basically right.

As with preformationism, so it was with special creation.
Here also absurd and unnecessary elaborations, with the
damping effect which these had upon scientific enquiry,
prepared the way for evolution. Evolution, like epigenesis,
acted for a while as a stimulant to biology. Once again,
no one noticed that it, also, like epigenesis, was fundamentally nothing more than a doctrine of spontaneous
generation spread out in time instead of being concentrated
into one life cycle and so was as fundamentally unscientific
as any perpetual motion machine.

When evolution is viewed in its historical perspective,
it is not difficult to understand why it, like its counterpart
epigenesis, has had so long a vogue. The doctrine of
special creation was overthrown three-quarters of a century
after preformationism and a corresponding delay in rever-
sion to the saner aspects of the earlier views on the origin
of species is only to be expected. Evolution presents a far
more baffling problem than the development of the embryo,
for it rests upon conjecture rather than upon direct observation. It is not unnatural that developments of thought
relating to the origins of species should repeat those relating
to embryology, but with a considerable lag between them.

Nevertheless, the time is now clearly ripe for the aban-
donment of the creative evolution hypothesis. And it
may well be asked why it is that some scientists, in their
public utterances, still assure the public that creative evolution is a proved fact.

The answer is two-fold. In the first place, although
some of the older generation of biologists still adhere
tenaciously to the Darwinian creed, it is not difficult to
detect a vein of profound scepticism in the writings and
conversation of the younger generation of scientists. But
the reason why evolution is rarely attacked is almost

certainly to be found in another direction.   Let us take an analogy.   Why is it that scientists in general are so profoundly unwilling to commit themselves on the subject of psychical research ?   Why is it that they often refuse quite ostentatiously to take any interest in the matter at all ?   The reason surely is that the subject has been largely monopolized by credulous spiritualists, who are prepared to believe almost anything, and who give their wholehearted support to fraudulent and covetous mediums. Scientists know that any fair-minded study of the facts on their part, any admission that this or that phenomenon had been proved, would at once be given a twist in the spiritualist press and would only serve to worsen the "racket." When spiritualists are given an inch they take a yard.

Is the position in connexion with evolution so very different?   Anti-evolution propaganda casts doubt on the sincerity or intelligence of leading scientists; books are written with question-begging titles; stupid and dishonest arguments are constantly used by the narrowest school of "fundamentalists," in which facts are almost deliberately perverted.

"Fundamentalists repeatedly assured the public in debates with me," says Joseph McCabe, "that the theory of the evolution of the horse was based upon one fossil skeleton, that of Eohippus, and that this is really the skeleton of a Californian rat that was drowned in the Deluge."[1] A favourite argument is that evolution can be mathematically disproved as follows.   History shows that the human race doubles itself every 160–170 years, while evolutionists say, or are supposed to say, that man is 2,000,000 years old.   But in order to make " greater allowances than any self-respecting evolutionist could do without blushing," let us suppose that man only doubles in numbers once every 1,600 years.   Even then there would not be standing room upon the earth!   " The evolutionist cannot side-step

[1] *The Riddle of the Universe To-day*, 1934, p. 112.

this argument by a new guess."[1] By the same argument one might prove that fleas were created less than a century ago.

In another work[2], this time of considerable size, a chapter is entitled " The Great Pyramid *Versus* Evolution." The author invites his readers to " reason together," sitting down with the Almighty " in the pyramid lighted courts of truth," after which they will see at once that evolution is false !

Rubbish of this kind is more than enough to alienate all scientific sympathy.[3] Yet fundamentalists do invaluable work in keeping alive a core of opposition to evolution. But for their influence the harm caused by evolutionary teaching would certainly have been much greater than it was.

Finally, what of the future ? Evolution, whatever scientists may say about it, will clearly continue to be accepted for a long time to come owing to its association with political and quasi-religious creeds. To-day, we live in an age of transition. The old idea that evolution should be our guide in sociology has been long discredited. Its application to numerous sciences other than biology have all led to false conclusions. The doctrine of the inevitability of progress, a doctrine that once made it unthinkable that Europe would ever see war, has had a sorry set-back. It is too much to hope that we have seen the last of evolution as a propaganda weapon in modern war, but at least this use of the doctrine has been temporarily discredited in Europe. Time and time again, applications of evolutionary teaching outside biology have led to muddled thinking and immoral conduct. But mankind never learns the lesson.

To-day, a new doctrine is beginning to emerge. We

[1] The quotations are taken from *Evolution of Man Scientifically Disproved*, by W. A. Williams. In order to aid the circulation of this book, modern American business methods were applied with a vengeance. The book cost one dollar, but if the reader was prepared to sell one copy to a friend at this price, his own dollar would purchase two copies. Under other conditions his dollar might purchase as many as five copies ! [2] G. R. Riffert, *Great Pyramid Proof of God*, 1932.

[3] In France, where there has been little anti-evolutionary propaganda, and where evolution has not been closely linked to politics, evolution appears to be dying a natural death.

are told, as we were told before, that it is man's duty to help evolution.   But it is now realized that evolution is so slow that it cannot change the anatomy or mental faculties of human beings for millions of years at least.   If, therefore, evolutionary doctrines are to be applied to current problems, their outlet will have to be sought elsewhere.

With this end in view and, in order that the ends achieved by conscious planning may be included under the term *evolution*, evolution has now been defined as development of increasing independence of the environment and increasing co-ordination.   And the evolution of human society, we are told, tallies exactly with this definition.   Moreover, it has taken place as a result of an increase in the size of co-ordinated groups of individuals—families, clans, cities and nations.   Very well then, the next step in evolutionary progress must be a world-state and evolution must supply the ethical motive for the realization of such a state.   To this end the nineteenth century notion that good and bad stand only for acts which help or hinder evolutionary progress has been revived.

Such views, though sponsored for propaganda purposes by Julian Huxley, Needham, Waddington and others, seem hardly worthy of discussion.   As always, so now, the doctrine of evolution can be applied in whatever way one pleases : it affords a rationalization, not an argument.   The ardent nationalist also may point with equal confidence to the colossal prehistoric reptiles, brontosaurus and its colleagues, which perished because they passed their optimum size.   From this he may, if he chooses, draw the moral that nature does not favour units which have grown too large and he may urge that human societies, too, must have an optimum size beyond which they become clumsy and unworkable. Here, as always, evolution is a double-edged weapon.

The desirability or otherwise of a world state, as of everything else for that matter, must be decided on its merits.   It has nothing whatever to do with evolution— least of all with the quasi-magical conception of evolution which is still in vogue in many quarters. To invoke the " evolutionary outlook " generally means only that one is determined at all costs to justify by specious science what one wishes in any case to do or to believe.

To-day, evolution still stands primarily for an attitude of mind—and it is a dangerous and ugly one at that. It encourages pride and excitement which eventually lead to disillusionment and loss of peace of mind. It focuses attention on wild schemes for improvement which never materialize and makes men lose a sense of their limitations. " It leads man to attempt the impossible, and persistently to attempt the impossible is, in the social body as in individual life, a form of neurosis, a mental disease."[1]

Above all, the so-called " evolutionary outlook " is still exactly what Darwin made it—a substitute god. Though more a child of the wishes than any form of theism ever was, evolution is accepted by moderns chiefly as a means for repressing their religious needs. We are told on all hands that the modern man cannot believe in God because it is "unscientific" to do so or just because he cannot imagine what God is like. That it is even more unscientific to baptize the great problem of biology without even attempting to explain it is conveniently forgotten. Nor can emotionally-minded evolutionists even see that the creation theory *does* at least go some way towards providing a satisfying explanation of life, though its *modus operandi* is, of course, hidden from our view. As for the second difficulty, it is clearly superficial only. Moderns are willing enough to accept the existence of electrons, protons, neutrinos and what-not; they are satisfied enough when the physicists tell them that they ought not even to try to imagine what these entities may be like.

But we are wandering from our theme and entering new fields of discussion which should find their place at the beginning rather than at the end of a volume. Enough that we have told the story of evolution.

[1] Alec Brown, *In Search of Faith*, 1943.

SELECT BIBLIOGRAPHY

The following list, containing books written from various points of view, may be found useful to the general reader. With a few important exceptions, highly technical books, standard text-books and the older literature have been omitted. Inclusion here does not imply approval or disapproval; the list is simply factual and objective.

Historical and Religious

Baldwin, J. L., *A New Answer to Darwinism*, 1957 (Baldwin, Manhattan Bldgs, Chicago 5, Ill.). Theistic orthogenetic view.

Dillinberger, J., *Protestant Thought and Natural Science*, Collins, 1961.

Fothergill, P. G., *Evolution and the Christians*, Longmans, 1961.

Gillispie, C. C., *Genesis and Geology*, Harvard U.P. and O.U.P., 1951

Glass B., Temkin, O. and Straus, W. L. Jr., *Forerunners of Darwin*, O.U.P., 1959.

Hooykaas R., *Natural Law and Divine Miracle*, Leiden, 1959.

Lack, D., *Evolutionary Theory and Christian Belief*, Methuen, 1957.

Lovejoy, A. O., *Essays in the History of Ideas*, John Hopkins Pr. 1948.

Mascall, E. L., *Christian Theology and Natural Science*, Longmans, 1956.

Millhauser, M., *Just before Darwin*, 1962, (Wesleyan Univ. Press, Connecticut). On Robert Chambers and the *Vestiges*.

O'Connell, P., *Science of Today and the Problems of Genesis*, 1959 (Radio Replies Press Soc., St. Paul, Minn.); Roman Catholic: very interesting. Gives evidence that Peking man is a fraud.

Ramm, B., *The Christian View of Science and Scripture*, repr. 1965, The Paternoster Press.

Smethurst, A. F., *Modern Science and Christian Beliefs*, 1955.

Darwin, Huxley, Etc.

Barclay, V., *Darwin is not for Children*, Jenkins, 1950. Chap. 15 deals with the Fuegians whose culture was highly advanced, though Darwin supposed them to be nearer monkeys than men.

Foskett, D. J., Wilberforce and Huxley on Evolution. *Nature*, 1953, **172**, 920. Contemporary account of the B.A. meeting by Huxley.

Gray, Asa, *Darwiniana*, 1876. New ed. Ed. A. H. Dupree, O.U.P., 1964.

Irvine, W., *Apes, Angels and Victorians*, Weidenfeld, & Nicolson, 1955.

Pantin. C. F. A., *School Science Review*, 1950, **32**, 75, 197, 313.

Repercussions of Malthusianism and Darwinism

Barzun, J. M., *Darwin, Marx and Wagner : the fatal Legacy of Progress.* Secker and Warburg, 1942.

Boner, H. A., *Hungry Generations: the Nineteenth Century Case against Malthusianism.* Columbia U.P. and O.U.P., 1955.

Boyle, J., *Politics and Opinion in the Nineteenth Century.* Cape, 1954.

Hofstadter, R., *Social Darwinism in American Thought*, 1860–1925. Pennsylvania U.P. and O.U.P., 1945.

MacConnaughtey, G., Darwin and Social Darwinism, *Osiris*, 1950, **9**, 397.

Machin, A., *Darwin's Theory Applied to Mankind*. Longmans, 1937. [Foreword by Sir A. Keith. Statement of the view that war is biologically inevitable.

McGovern, W. M., *From Luther to Hitler: the History of Fascist-Nazi Political Philosophy*. Harrap, 1946.

Meek, R. L., *Marx and Engels on Malthus*, Lawrence & W., 1953.

Persons, S. [Ed.], *Evolutionary Thought in America*. Yale U.P., 1950.

Quillian, W. S., *The Moral Theory of Evolutionary Naturalism*. Yale U.P. and O.U.P., 1945.

Schneider, H. W., The Influence of Darwin and Spencer on American Philosophical Theology. *Jour. of the History of Ideas*, 1945, **6**, 1.

Smith, K., *The Malthusian Controversy*. Routledge & Kegan Paul, 1951.

Origin of Life: Design

Clark, R. E. D., *The Universe: Plan or Accident?* 3rd ed., 1961. Paternoster Press.

Dixon, M. and Webb, E. C., *Enzymes*, 2nd ed., C.U.P., 1964. Last chapter discusses difficulties of spontaneous origin of life.

Harris, R. J. C., The Origin of Life, *Jour. Trans. Victoria Institute*, 1949, **81**, 58.

Oparin A. I. (Ed.), *International Symposium on the Origin of Life, Moscow*, Pergamon Press, 1959. (Difficulties to be faced are minimized but often obvious between the lines. The less self-critical parts of this book reappeared as *Evolutionary Biochemistry*, Pergamon Press, 1963, which is much less expensive.)

Pantin, C. F. A., Organic Design. (Press. Add. to Section D, B.A., 1951) *Advancement of Science*, **8**, 138.

Short, A. R., *Wonderfully Made*, repr. 1964, The Paternoster Press.

General Books

Davies, A. Morley, *Evolution and its Modern Critics*, 1937.

Dewar, D., *Difficulties of the Evolution Theory*, 1931: Papers in *Jour. Trans., Victoria Institute*: and L. M. Davies, *Is Evolution a Myth?* A debate with J. B. S. Haldane, Watts and Paternoster Press, 1949; *Is Evolution Proved?* A debate with H. S. Shelton, Ed. Arnold Lunn, 1947; *The Transformist Illusion*, 1959 (Dehoff Publications, Murfreesboro, Tennessee).

Doyle, J., *Advancement of Science*, 1957, **14**, 120. B.A., Presidential Sectional Address (Botany). Natural selection is inadequate in botany.

Ehrlich, P. R. and Holm, R. W., *The Process of Evolution*, McGraw-Hill, 1963.

Huxley, J. (Sir), *Evolution, the Modern Synthesis*, Allen & Unwin, 1963 ed. With Hardy, A. C. and Ford, E. B., *Evolution as a Process*, Allen & Unwin, 1954.

Simons, E. L., The Early Relatives of Man. *Scientific American*, July 1964. (Shows that definite evidence for such relatives is lacking).

Simpson, G. G., *The Major Features of Evolution*, Columbia U.P., 1953.

Society for Experimental Biology, Symposium No. 7, *Evolution*, 1953.

Tax, Sol (Ed.), *Evolution after Darwin*, 3 Vols. (Univ. of Chicago Pr.) A mine of information by many authors.

Theory of Natural Selection Today, The, *Nature*, 1959. Articles.

INDEX—(*Subjects are in italics.*)